MULTIPLE CHOICE
QUIZZES

THE QUIZ BOOK COMPANY

First published in 2004 by
The Quiz Book Company Ltd
Bardfield Centre,
Great Bardfield, Essex, CM7 4SL

ISBN 1-84236-506-1

Printed in India

Questions written by Chris Rigby

BRON-Y-WENDON
• HOLIDAY PARKS •
NANT-Y-GLYN

QUIZ 1

1 Tarquin the Proud was the last king of where?
   Macedonia, Rome, Troy

2 Which film ended with the line, "I used to hate
   water, I can't imagine why"? *Titanic*, *Jaws*, *The
   Poseidon Adventure*

3 What is the last book of the Old Testament?
   Numbers, Malachi, Judges

4 Who rode his last Epsom Derby winner in 1994?
   Lester Piggott, Pat Eddery, Willie Carson

5 Who plays Nathen Algren in *The Last Samurai*?
   Matt Damon, Tom Cruise, Orlando Bloom

6 Which novel was originally entitled, *The Last Man
   In Europe*? *1984*, *Last Of The Mohicans*, *Don Juan*

7 The 1994 film *Backfire* marked the last screen
   appearance of which actor, famed for playing a TV
   detective? Peter Falk, Barry Foster, Telly Savalas

8 Which song was a hit for both Wham and
   Whigfield? 'Last Night', 'Last Christmas', 'Last Train'

9 Which US President's last words were, "I have a
   terrific headache"? Abraham Lincoln, George
   Washington, Franklin D Roosevelt

10 In what year of the 1900s did man last set foot on
   the moon? 1972, 1969, 1970

ANSWERS

1. Rome 2. *Jaws* 3. Malachi 4. Willie Carson 5. Tom Cruise 6. *1984* 7. Telly
Savalas 8. 'Last Christmas' 9. Franklin D Roosevelt 10. 1972

QUIZ 2

. . . .

1 In a calendar year, how many months have exactly thirty days? Four, Five, Seven

2 In the nursery rhyme, what happened to Solomon Grundy on a Tuesday? Christened, Died, Married

3 Which organ of the body produces anti-bodies? Liver, Spleen, Colon

4 What word represents the letter Y in the NATO phonetic alphabet? Yankee, Yacht, Yeti

5 What is the 45th wedding anniversary? China, Coral, Sapphire

6 What is a Portuguese man o' war? Jellyfish, Card game, Soldier

7 What saint's day falls on November 30th? George, Andrew, Patrick

8 What is the home town of Crocodile Dundee? Cooper's Crossing, Walkabout Creek, Outback Ridge

9 What is the 12th sign of the zodiac? Pisces, Aries, Leo

10 What is a pelisse? A Fruit, A cloak, A frog

ANSWERS

1. Four 2. Christened 3. Spleen 4. Yankee 5. Sapphire 6. Jellyfish 7. Andrew
8. Walkabout Creek 9. Pisces 10. A cloak

QUIZ 3

- -

1 Which TV sitcom featured a butler called Alf Stokes? *The Addams Family*, *To The Manor Born*, *You Rang M'Lord*

2 What animal is in the title sequence of One Foot In The Grave? Ape, Tortoise, Squirrel

3 Who played Father Noel Furlong in Father Ted? Graham Norton, Dermot Morgan, Ardal O'Hanlon

4 What is the name of the café in Friends? Café Nervosa, Central Perk, Dip And Sip

5 What breed of dog is Duke in The Beverly Hillbillies? Afghan, Mastiff, Bloodhound

6 Who did Harold Bennett play in *Are You Being Served*? Young Mr Grace, Captain Peacock, Mr Rumbold

7 Which TV comedy featured Speed, Tucker and Wolfie? *Open All Hours*, *Porridge*, *Citizen Smith*

8 What is the name of the chef in Fawlty Towers? Terry, Tony, Tex

9 The sitcom *Get Some In* was set in which branch of the armed forces? Army, Navy, RAF?

10 Who played Lieutenant George Barleigh in *Blackadder Goes Forth*? Tony Robinson, Stephen Fry, Hugh Laurie

ANSWERS

1. *You Rang M'Lord* 2. Tortoise 3. Graham Norton 4. Central Perk
5. Bloodhound 6. Young Mr Grace 7. *Citizen Smith* 8. Terry 9. RAF
10. Hugh Laurie

QUIZ 4

. . . .

1 What does a seismologist study? Caves, Earthquakes, Mountains

2 The word monsoon is derived from the Arabic for what? Flood, Season, Storm

3 What is London's largest park? Hyde Park, Regent's Park, St James Park

4 The Great Smoo is Scotland's largest what? Mountain, Loch, Cave

5 In which film did Gregory Peck play Captain Ahab? *Moby Dick, Sinbad The Sailor, Mutiny On The Bounty*

6 Which organisation was founded by Chad Vara in the 1950s? Samaritans, Greenpeace, NATO

7 In heraldry what shape is a mullet? Diamond, Star, Shield

8 What is the coldest planet in the Solar System? Neptune, Uranus, Pluto

9 BSL is the airport code of which city? Bratislava, Basle, Brasilia

10 Whose daily diary entries ended with the words, "And so to bed"? Adrian Mole, Anne Frank, Samuel Pepys

ANSWERS

1. Earthquakes 2. Season 3. Hyde Park 4. Cave 5. *Moby Dick* 6. Samaritans
7. Star 8. Pluto 9. Basle 10. Samuel Pepys

QUIZ 5

• •

The following are morbid fears of what?

1 Carnophobia   Meat, Motor Vehicles, Fun Fairs

2 Halophobia   Priests, Wheels, Speaking

3 Ailurophobia   Dogs, Cats, Mice

4 Ombrophobia   Rain, Snow, Fog

5 Pyrophobia   Fire, Water, Soil

6 Melophobia   Fruit, Surgery, Music,

7 Pogonophobia   Teletubbies, Beards, Ladders

8 Chromophobia   Metals, Colour, Mirrors

9 Triskaidekaphobia   The number 13, Bicycles, Monkeys

10 Demophobia   Satan, Eating, Crowds

ANSWERS

QUIZ 6

. . . .

1 Which day of the year is St Stephen's Day?   May Day, Boxing Day, Twelfth Night

2 What is the last name of Clive Dunn's character in *Dad's Army*?   Jones, Smith, Wilson

3 Which English city had the Roman name of Deva? Cambridge, Chester, Durham

4 Which actor played twin brothers in the film *Dead Ringers*?   John Lithgow, Jeremy Irons, James Caan

5 What is the home planet of Dr Who?   Phobos, Vulcan, Gallifrey

6 Which organisation has its headquarters at Langley, Virginia in the USA?   CIA, FBI, Greenpeace

7 Which of the Teletubbies is yellow? La La, Dipsy, Tinky Winky

8 What does the DK stand for with regard to the fashion empire DKNY?   David Kelly, Donna Karan, Debonair Kit

9 Which country is home to the Tivoli Gardens? Romania, Croatia, Denmark

10 What does the W stand for in the name of George W Bush?   Walker, William, Walt

ANSWERS

1. Boxing Day 2. Jones 3. Chester 4. Jeremy Irons 5. Gallifrey 6. CIA 7. La La
8. Donna Karan 9. Denmark 10. Walker

QUIZ 7

• •

1 Which Shakespeare play features the line, "Neither a lender or a borrower be"? *The Merchant Of Venice*, *Hamlet*, *King Lear*

2 What is the name of Scarlet O'Hara's home in Gone With The Wind? Lara, Dora, Tara

3 What type of animal is Benjamin Bouncer in the Beatrix Potter tales? Dog, Deer, Rabbit

4 Who made his literary debut in the story A Study In Scarlet? Perry Mason, Hercule Poirot, Sherlock Holmes

5 Who wrote the novel *Villette*? Charlotte Bronte, Anne Bronte, Branwell Bronte

6 Which literary doctor was created by AJ Cronin? Dr Doolittle, Dr Finlay, Dr Jekyl

7 Which Dickens novel features the character of Mr Bumble? *Oliver Twist*, *Hard Times*, *Bleak House*

8 What is the first name of The Saint, the literary creation of Leslie Charteris? Ian, Ted, Simon

9 Who fell asleep in a tea-pot in Alice's Adventures In Wonderland? The Dormouse, Alice, Mock Turtle

10 What was the first James Bond novel? *Dr No*, *Casino Royale*, *You Only Live Twice*

ANSWERS

1. *Hamlet* 2. Tara 3. Rabbit 4. Sherlock Holmes 5. Charlotte Bronte 6. Dr Finlay 7. *Oliver Twist* 8. Simon 9. The Dormouse 10. *Casino Royale*

QUIZ 8

1 How many provinces are there in Canada? 10, 15, 20

2 What does the T stand for with regard to the triple vaccine DTP? Typhoid, Tetanus, Tonsillitis

3 What bird provides the nickname of Norwich City FC? Canary, Robin, Swan

4 Which word means the opposite of evergreen? Conifer, Deciduous, Perennial

5 Fisherman's Bend and Cat's Paw are both types of what? Lobster, Mushroom, Knot

6 What was the name of the building outside of which John Lennon was murdered? Carolina, Dakota, Delaware

7 Who played the role of Tuko in *The Good, The Bad And The Ugly*? Eli Wallach, James Coburn, Clint Eastwood

8 What name is given to the central space in a church? Apse, Nave, Rectory

9 What type of weapon is an assegai? Axe, Sword, Spear

10 Hollywood is a suburb of which city? New York, Chicago, Los Angeles

ANSWERS

1. 10 2. Tetanus 3. Canary 4. Deciduous 5. Knot 6. Dakota building
7. Eli Wallach 8. Nave 9. Spear 10. Los Angeles

QUIZ 9

• •

1 A nephogram is a photograph of what? Star, Cloud, Comet

2 On which planet is The Great Red Spot? Mars, Jupiter, Mercury

3 What does a cubic decimetre equate to? A kilometre, a centimetre, a litre

4 What does a limnologist study? Lightning, Lakes, Constellations

5 What is the more common name for nitrous oxide? Dry ice, Laughing gas, Krypton

6 What does the Ph stand for with regard to the Ph scale? Positive helium, Potential hydrogen, Potassium high

7 What element derives its name from the Greek word for green? Bromide, Neon, Chlorine

8 What measures ten on the Beaufort Scale? Storm, Gale, Hurricane

9 What is the more common name for calcium carbonate? Talcum powder, Chalk, Epsom salts

10 What gas has the atomic number of one? Helium, Hydrogen, Oxygen

ANSWERS

1. Cloud 2. Jupiter 3. A litre 4. Lakes 5. Laughing gas 6. Potential hydrogen
7. Chlorine 8. Storm 9. Chalk 10. Hydrogen

QUIZ 10

. . . .

1 What name is derived from the Arabic for crown?
   Simon, Steven, Spencer

2 What is the alternative name for the snow
   leopard?   Cougar, Bobcat, Ounce

3 The Mossad is the secret service of which
   country?   South Africa, Israel, Egypt

4 Which food item is named after the French word
   for crescent?   Meringue, Croissant, Bagel

5 In the Muppet Show, what is the last name of
   Miss Piggy? Back, Banks, Lee

6 What type of musical instrument is a bissex?
   Guitar, Piano, Violin

7 Desiree and King Edward are both varieties of
   which vegetable? Potato, Parsnip, Pea

8 What name is given to an angle between 180 and
   360 degrees?   Obtuse, Reflex, Acute

9 The Leap Frog and The Ampleforth are both types
   of what?   Chess moves, Morris Dance, Tanks

10 Who did George Cole portray in the *St Trinians*
    films?   Smart Alec, Flash Harry, Dodgy Dave

ANSWERS

1. Steven 2. Ounce 3. Israel 4. Croissant 5. Lee 6. Guitar 7. Potato 8. Reflex
9. Morris Dance 10. Flash Harry

QUIZ 11

• •

1 Genevieve is the patron saint of where? New York, Paris, London

2 Dunstan is the patron saint of which profession? Butchers, Blacksmiths, Candlestick makers

3 Olaf is the patron saint of which country? Sweden, Finland, Norway

4 Boniface is the patron saint of which country? France, Germany, Netherlands

5 What is Ambrose the patron saint of? Beekeepers, Lion tamers, Sheep shearers

6 What is Jude the patron saint of? The Beatles, Lost causes, Bridegrooms

7 Giles is the patron saint of which British city? Liverpool, Belfast, Edinburgh

8 What is Sebastian the patron saint of? Athletes, Portugal, Prison officers

9 What is Agatha the patron saint of? Volcanoes, Authors, Nuns

10 What is Clare the patron saint of? Television, Headaches, Drunks

ANSWERS

1. Paris 2. Blacksmiths 3. Norway 4. Germany 5. Beekeepers 6. Lost causes
7. Edinburgh 8. Athletes 9. Volcanoes 10. Television

QUIZ 12

. . . .

1 On which continent did guinea pigs originate?
   Africa, Australia, South America

2 What is the name of the highest civil decoration
   in France? Parisian Cross, Legion of Honour, Order
   of DeGaulle

3 What word completes the saying, Marry in haste
   and repent at …? Once, Leisure, Court

4 How many wives of Henry VIII were executed?
   One, Two, Four

5 What is gynophobia the fear of? Alcohol, Speed,
   Women

6 Which snake was depicted on the crowns of
   Egyptian pharoahs? Asp, Viper, Cobra

7 As worn by Greek soldiers, what is a fustanella?
   Helmet, Skirt, Jacket

8 What is the actual meaning of Kung Fu? Dragon
   style, Gentle way, Leisure time

9 Which stadium was built for the London Olympics
   of 1908? White City, Wembley, Crystal Palace,

10 What is a funambulist? Tightrope walker, Sleep
    walker, Ice skater

ANSWERS

1. South America 2. Legion of Honour 3. Leisure 4. Two 5. Women
6. Cobra 7. Skirt 8. Leisure time 9. White City 10. Tightrope walker

QUIZ 13

1. Ladywood is a district of which British city?
   Swansea, Birmingham, Leeds

2. Which county is home to the Highgrove royal
   residents? Glamorgan, Gloucestershire, Surrey

3. In which county is the carpet manufacturing
   town of Axminster located? Devon, Cornwall,
   Dorset

4. Which island houses the Tynwald Parliament? Isle
   Of Wight, Isle Of Man, Anglesey

5. What is the symbol of the British National Trust?
   Avocet, Oak leaf, Badger

6. Which month shares its name with a town in
   Cambridgeshire? August, March, May

7. In which city is the Clifton Suspension Bridge?
   Bristol, Bradford, Southampton

8. In which country does the River Seven rise?
   England, Northern Ireland, Wales

9. In which decade did Gatwick Airport open?
   1950s, 1960s, 1970s

10. Which football club's ground is home to the
    National Football Museum? Preston North End,
    Burnley, Blackpool

ANSWERS

1. Birmingham 2. Gloucestershire 3. Devon 4. Isle Of Man 5. Oak leaf
6. March 7. Bristol 8. Wales 9. 1950s 10. Preston North End

QUIZ 14

• •

1 Mittwoch is the German word for which day of the week? Wednesday, Friday, Sunday

2 Which Irish county is divided into ridings? Cork, Limerick, Tipperary

3 In which month of the year is the FA Cup final traditionally contested? April, May, June

4 In which room was Janet Leigh murdered in the film *Psycho*? Bathroom, Bedroom, Study

5 Car seat belts were established in which country? Sweden, France, Spain

6 On a computer keyboard which letter of the alphabet is sandwiched by E and T? R, S, W

7 What does the V stand for in the acronym VAT? Variable, Visual, Value

8 From which language does the word alphabet derive? French, Arabic, Greek

9 Which expanse of water does St Andrew's golf course overlook? Loch Ness, North Sea, Loch Lomond

10 In which category did Winston Churchill receive a Nobel Prize? Economics, Literature, Peace

ANSWERS

1. Wednesday 2. Tipperary 3. May 4. Bathroom 5. Spain 6. R 7. Value 8. Greek 9. North Sea 10. Literature

QUIZ 15

1 Who took his name from a 1963 film with Albert Finney?   Sting, Adam Faith, Tom Jones

2 Which brothers had chart success with Make It Easy On Yourself?   Righteous Brothers, Bellamy Brothers, Walker Brothers

3 Who collaborated with Paul McCartney on the song 'Say Say Say'?   Michael Jackson, John Lennon, Van Morrison

4 What was pop group Edison Lighthouse's only number one hit?   'Love Is All Around', 'Love Grows', 'Love In The First Degree'

5 Who presented the 2001 Brit Awards?   Ant & Dec, Baddiel & Skinner, French & Saunders

6 Whose hit was 'Love Won't Wait'?   Mark Owen, Robbie Williams, Gary Barlow

7 Who had a hit with 'Just Walking In The Rain'? Johnnie Ray, Bobby Darin, Frankie Laine

8 Which US group was formed by Ann and Nancy Wilson?   The Go Go's, Wilson Phillips, Heart

9 In which country was Bonnie Tyler born? England, Ireland, Wales

10 What was glam rockers Sweet's only number one hit?   'Blockbuster', 'Coco', 'Wig Wam Bam'

ANSWERS

1. Tom Jones 2. Walker Brothers 3. Michael Jackson 4. 'Love Grows'
5. Ant & Dec 6. Gary Barlow 7. Johnnie Ray 8. Heart 9. Wales
10. 'Blockbuster'

QUIZ 16

1 What is theophobia the fear of?   Policemen, Mathematics, God

2 What is a cutlass?   Sword, Sail, Wine glass

3 In which film did Kevin Costner play the role of Jim Garrison?   *JFK*, *The Bodyguard*, *Body Heat*

4 In which county is the TV comedy series *Last Of The Summer Wine* set?   Kent , Cornwall, Yorkshire

5 Which car manufacturer has made models called the Tempra and the Tipo?   Audi, Fiat, Citröen

6 What is crossbred with a cow to make a dzo?   Elk, Buffalo, Yak

7 What is the largest lake in England?   Windermere, Ullswater, Coniston

8 What constitutes approximately 12 percent of an egg's weight?   Yolk, Shell, White

9 In which film did Sean Connery play the role of Juan Sanchez Villa- Lobos Ramirez?   *Highlander*, *Time Bandits*, *Rising Sun*

10 What was the only Grand Slam singles title that Virginia Wade did not win?   Wimbledon, French Open, Australian Open

ANSWERS

1. God 2. Sword 3. *JFK* 4. Yorkshire 5. Fiat 6. Yak 7. Windermere 8. Shell
9. *Highlander* 10. French Open

QUIZ 17

• •

1 Which US city is home to the Liberty Bell?
   Phoenix, Philadelphia, Washington DC,

2 In which US city is the comedy series *Seinfeld* set?
   Boston, New York, Detroit

3 IA is the zip code for which US state?   Indiana,
   Idaho, Iowa

4 In what decade was slavery abolished in the USA?
   1860s, 1870s, 1880s

5 The name of which US state is derived from the
   Spanish for mountain?   Maine, Montana, Missouri

6 What became the 50th state of the union?   New
   Mexico, Hawaii, Alaska

7 In which borough of New York is Wall Street
   located?   Queens, Manhattan, The Bronx

8 Which US state is bordered by Georgia and
   Alabama? Utah, Florida, Texas

9 What is the most highly populated city in
   California? Sacramento, San Jose, Los Angeles

10 How many states of the USA border Alaska?
    None, One, Four

ANSWERS

1. Philadelphia 2. New York 3. Iowa 4. 1860s 5. Montana 6. Hawaii
7. Manhattan 8. Florida 9. Los Angeles 10. None

QUIZ 18

. . . .

1 On which island was Ben Gunn marooned? Coral Island, Pitcairn Island, Treasure Island

2 What item of food has a name that literally means, bits and pieces? Kebab, Chop Suey, Chow Mein

3 What does a bowler attempt to hit in a game of French cricket? Wickets, Walls, Legs

4 In the human body what is the non technical name for the hallux? ear, big toe, elbow

5 What is the last letter of the Greek alphabet? Zeta, Omega, Xi

6 What does the I stand for in the acronym CID? Intelligence, Internal, Investigation

7 In Moscow, what is the Tsar Kolokol? A bell, A tower, A cannon

8 Which wife of Henry VIII was known as The Flanders Mare? Catharine of Aragon, Anne of Cleves, Jane Seymour

9 When was the Bank of England founded? 1500s, 1600s, 1700s

10 In which city is the TV drama series *Porterhouse Blue* set? Cambridge, London, Oxford

ANSWERS

1. Treasure Island 2. Chop Suey 3. Legs 4. Big toe 5. Omega
6. Investigation 7. A bell 8. Anne of Cleves 9. 1600s 10. Oxford

QUIZ 19

. . . .

1 What type of animal is Pummba in The Lion King?
   Baboon, Warthog, Hyena

2 Who is the son of King Randor?   Dangermouse,
   He-Man, Gadget Boy

3 What does the tattoo depict on Popeye's arm?
   Anchor, Spinach, Mermaid

4 In The Simpsons what is Marge Simpson's maiden
   name? Bouvier, Nixon, Ford

5 What is the home town of Fred Flintstone?
   Stonecave, Cobbletown, Bedrock

6 Which cartoon character was often heard singing
   'My Darling Clementine'?   Huckleberry Hound,
   Foghorn Leghorn, Speedy Gonzales

7 In which US state is South Park set?   Texas, Utah,
   Colorado

8 Yosemite Sam is the arch-enemy of which cartoon
   character?   Sylvester the Cat, Bugs Bunny, Quick
   Draw McGraw

9 Which actor provided the voice of Dangermouse?
   John Thaw, Martin Clunes, David Jason

10 In which decade did Popeye make his cartoon
    debut?   1920s, 1930s, 1950s

ANSWERS

1. Warthog 2. He-Man 3. Anchor 4. Bouvier 5. Bedrock 6. Huckleberry
Hound 7. Colorado 8. Bugs Bunny 9. David Jason 10. 1920s

QUIZ 20

1 Which city's population first exceeded one million? Bombay, London, Tokyo

2 Which road was a hit album for Paul Weller? *Baker Street*, *Electric Avenue*, *Stanley Road*

3 Which *Carry On* film chronicled the exploits of a highwayman? *Carry On Dick*, *Carry On Jack*, *Carry On Screaming*

4 Which fashion designer introduced the New Look in 1947? Coco Chanel, Christian Dior, Yves St Laurent

5 What word is the superlative of strong? Weak, Stronger, Strongest

6 What does the L stand for in LSD? Lethal, Lithium, Lysergic

7 Which film featured a space craft called Discovery One? *2001 A Space Odyssey*, *Alien*, *Contact*

8 Who yelled, "Off with her head" in Alice In Wonderland? Queen Of Clubs, Queen Of Hearts, Queen Of Diamonds

9 What is the nationality of the painter Salvador Dali? Spanish, Italian, French

10 SEL is the airport code for which city? Seattle, Seoul, Stockholm

ANSWERS

1. London 2. *Stanley Road* 3. *Carry On Dick* 4. Christian Dior 5. Strongest
6. Lysergic 7. *2001 A Space Odyssey* 8. Queen Of Hearts 9. Spanish
10. Seoul

QUIZ 21

• •

1 In what year was the OPEC oil organisation founded?   1941, 1961, 1971,

2 What year witnessed the Challenger space shuttle tragedy?   1984, 1985, 1986

3 In what year was the Great Fire Of London?   1656, 1665, 1666

4 In what year of the 1990s was the Grand National abandoned due to a false start?   1993, 1997, 1999

5 In what year did Queen Elizabeth II marry Prince Philip?   1947, 1948, 1951

6 In what year was the Greenpeace ship The Rainbow Warrior sunk?   1981, 1985, 1987

7 What year witnessed the bombing of Pearl Harbor in World War II?   1940, 1941, 1943

8 In what year was the Sky Digital TV channel launched?   1994, 1998, 2000

9 In what year did Nadia Comaneci become the first gymnast to score a perfect 10?   1976, 1978, 1982

10 What year did Great Britain join the EEC?   1973, 1975, 1977

ANSWERS

1. 1961 2. 1986 3. 1666 4. 1993 5. 1947 6. 1985 7. 1941 8. 1998 9. 1976
10. 1973

QUIZ 22

• •

1 In Only Fools And Horses, in which House is the Trotters' flat?   George Washington, Nelson Mandela, Horatio Nelson

2 Who was the Roman Emperor when Jesus Christ was crucified?   Augustus, Tiberius, Claudius

3 Where did the pop group Madness catch a night boat to?   Moscow, Cairo, Oslo

4 The sitcom *George And Mildred* was a spin off from which TV show?   *Bless This House*, *Love Thy Neighbour*, *Man About The House*

5 What is the alternative name for a cor anglais? Sousaphone, Bassoon, English horn

6 Juneau is the state capital of which US state? Alaska, South Dakota, Vermont

7 If mach 1 equal supersonic, what does mach 5 equal?   Megasonic, Hypersonic, Subsonic

8 In which Irish county can one kiss the Blarney Stone?   Cork, Kildaire, Waterford

9 In which film did Rocky Balboa fight Ivan Drago? *Rocky II*, *Rocky III*, *Rocky IV*

10 Which US landmark witnessed the climax of Hitchcock's North By North West?   Empire State Building, Statue Of Liberty, Mount Rushmore

ANSWERS

1. Nelson Mandela House 2. Tiberius 3. Cairo 4. *Man About The House*
5. English horn 6. Alaska 7. Hypersonic 8. Cork 9. *Rocky IV* 10. Mount Rushmore

QUIZ 23

1. Which musical instrument is nicknamed the pretzel? Trombone, Trumpet, French horn

2. Which TV show featured a band called Dr Teeth and The Electric Mayhem Band? *The Muppet Show*, *Ally McBeal*, *Fame*

3. What musical instrument did Russ Conway play? Trumpet, Piano, Guitar

4. Who composed the opera Don Giovanni? Bizet, Mozart, Vivaldi

5. Which group had hits with 'Strange Town' and 'Start'? The Jam, Honeyz, Bread

6. Which wild west hero is associated with The William Tell Overture? Hopalong Cassidy, The Virginian, The Lone Ranger

7. What name is given to the principle female singer of an opera? Prima Donna, Diva, Soprano

8. In which city was Andre Previn born? Venice, Berlin, New York

9. In which country is the Gilbert & Sullivan opera The Mikado set? Italy, China, Japan

10. Who had hits with 'Sherry' and 'Walk Like A Man'? Four Aces, Four Seasons, Four Tops

ANSWERS

1. French horn 2. *The Muppet Show* 3. Piano 4. Mozart 5. The Jam 6. The Lone Ranger 7. Prima Donna 8. Berlin 9. Japan 10. Four Seasons

QUIZ 24

. . . .

1 What is the Confederation of Helvetica better known as? Greece, Switzerland, Albania

2 In which film did Maggie Smith play the Countess of Trentham? *Sister Act, Gosford Park, A Room With A View*

3 What is the capital of Guernsey? St Paul Port, St Simon Port, St Peter Port

4 What would a person's star sign be if born on October 17? Libra, Scorpio, Virgo

5 Who penned an autobiography entitled V Is For Victory? Harvey Smith, Eric Cantona, Horatio Nelson

6 What was Oliver Twist's original surname? Brownlow, Fleming, Dawkins

7 In which US state is the city of Nashville located? Texas, Tennessee, Arkansas

8 What does a protactor measure? Angles, Temperature, Radiation

9 How are Sabrina, Kelly and Jill collectively known in the title of a TV series? *The Golden Girls, The Avengers, Charlie's Angels*

10 What animal laughed in the nursery rhyme Hey Diddle Diddle? Cat, Dog, Mouse

ANSWERS

1. Switzerland 2 *Gosford Park* 3. St Peter Port 4. Libra 5. Harvey Smith
6 Fleming 7. Tennessee 8 Angles 9. *Charlie's Angels* 10 Dog

QUIZ 25

• •

1 According to the proverb, fine words butter no what? Potatoes, Parsnips, Toast

2 What are the petals of a flower collectively known as? Petula, Corolla, Stamen

3 What is the singular of data? Dato, Datest, Datum

4 Which of the following literary characters could be described as "cheeseparing"? Scrooge, James Bond, Billy Bunter

5 From which language did the word robot originate? Russian, Czechoslovakian, Italian

6 What animal does the adjective vulpine refer to? Wolf, Fox, Vulture

7 What does a deltiologist collect? Beer mats, Postcards, Teeth

8 What does the word renaissance literally mean? Replay, Reaction, Rebirth

9 What name is given to the highest order of angels? Guardian, Arch, Seraphim

10 Which word of Italian origin literally means blood feud? Gladiator, Vendetta, Mafia

ANSWERS

1. Parsnips 2. Corolla 3. Datum 4. Scrooge 5. Czechoslovakian 6 Fox
7. Postcards 8. Rebirth 9. Seraphim 10. Vendetta

QUIZ 26

. . . .

1 What is the largest borough in New York?
   Brooklyn, The Bronx, Queens

2 In which TV series did Peter Graves play the role
   of Jim Phelps? *I Spy, Dragnet, Mission Impossible*

3 What is the largest island in the Mediterranean
   Sea? Malta, Sicily, Sardinia

4 In which decade was the Golden Gate Bridge
   opened in San Francisco? 1920s, 1930s, 1950s

5 Pica Pica is the Latin name for which bird?
   Kestrel, Magpie, Raven

6 In the Conan Doyle novels, what is the name of
   the brother of Sherlock Holmes? Henry, Marvin,
   Mycroft

7 Who wrote the first book of the New Testament?
   John, Matthew, Mark

8 Which island is inhabited by Bejans? Barbados,
   Borneo, Bermuda

9 Which letter of the alphabet is denoted by a
   single dot in Morse Code? A, E, I

10 In which decade was Isaac Newton born? 1620s,
   1640s, 1660s

ANSWERS

1. Queens 2. *Mission Impossible* 3. Sicily 4. 1930s 5. Magpie 6. Mycroft
7. Matthew 8. Barbados 9. E 10. 1640s

QUIZ 27

. . . .

1 By 2004, how many Popes have abdicated?   One, Five, Twenty

2 What surname was shared by the second and sixth President of the USA?   Harrison, Adams, Wilson

3 In which century did Peeping Tom peep at Lady Godiva?   10th, 11th, 13th

4 The Roman road Cassian Way linked Rome with which city?   Pompeii, Florence, Paris

5 Who designed the uniform of the Swiss Guard? Michelangelo, Rembrandt, Monet

6 For how many days did Lady Jane Grey rule England?   9, 19, 29

7 Who led the victorious troops at the Battle of Stirling Bridge?   Rob Roy, William Wallace, Robert The Bruce

8 Who was the last Holy Roman Emperor? Ferdinand II, Francis II, Umberto II

9 Who was the first Tudor monarch?   Edward IV, Richard III, Henry VII

10 At the start of the 21st century, who was the first princess in line to the British throne?   Anne, Beatrice, Margaret

ANSWERS

1. One 2. Adams 3. 11th 4. Florence 5. Michelangelo 6. 9 7. William Wallace 8. Francis II 9. Henry VII 10. Princess Beatrice

QUIZ 28

. . . .

1 What are used to predict the future in cartomancy? Twigs, Smoke, Tarot Cards

2 Castlebar is the capital of which Irish county? Donegal, Mayo, Kilkenny

3 A pandemonium is the collective noun for a group of what? Parrots, Apes, Seagulls

4 What does the culinary term farci mean? Served cold, Stuffed, Fried

5 What is the nationality of Franz Hals, the painter of the Laughing Cavalier? Austrian, Dutch, French

6 What does an apiphobic person fear? Apes, Birds, Bees

7 In the sport of golf, what is presented to the winner of the US Masters? Gold cap, Green jacket, Black tie

8 The seaport of Split lies on which sea? Adriatic, Caspian, Baltic

9 In what year did Red Rum first triumph in the Grand National? 1973, 1974, 1978

10 Which film earned Dustin Hoffman his first Best Actor Oscar? *Tootsie*, *The Graduate*, *Kramer Vs Kramer*

ANSWERS

1. Tarot Cards 2. Mayo 3. Parrots 4. Stuffed 5. Dutch 6. Bees 7. Green jacket 8. Adriatic 9. 1973 10. *Kramer Vs Kramer*

QUIZ 29

1 What part of the body is supplied with blood by the carotid artery?   Heart, Head, Arm

2 Which organ of the body produces insulin? Kidney, Liver, Pancreas

3 What is the more common name for the patella? Shoulder blade, Kneecap, Skull

4 If a person is anosmic, what sense is missing? Smell, Hearing, Taste

5 What is Cockney rhyming slang for the feet? Cover and sheet, Trick or treat, Plates of meat

6 What is the non technical name for the trachea? Windpipe, Voice box, Tonsils

7 What does a rhinologist study?   Ears, Teeth, Nose

8 What are inflamed in the disease phlebitis?   Feet, Gums, Veins

9 What is the longest bone in the human body? Tibia, Femur, Humerus

10 What do Isihara charts test?   Reflexes, ESP, Colour blindness

ANSWERS

1. Head 2. Pancreas 3. Kneecap 4. Smell 5. Plates of meat 6. Windpipe
7. Nose 8. Veins 9. Femur 10. Colour blindness

QUIZ 30

. . . .

1 Which US city is nicknamed The Big D? Dallas, Denver, Dover

2 In which sport did Clive Woodward win 21 caps for England? Cricket, Football, Rugby Union

3 Which Womble shares his name with a town on the island of Mull? Wellington, Cholet, Tobermory

4 Which planet of the Solar System is nearest in size to Earth? Neptune, Venus, Mars

5 What did Liam Gallagher name his son in honour of one of The Beatles? Paul, Harrison, Lennon

6 Which island is served by Ronaldsway Airport? Guernsey, Jersey, Isle Of Man

7 In which country was Dawn French born? England, Wales, France

8 What was the screen cowboy Gene Autry's horse called? Champion, Trigger, Scout

9 What are stored in a humidor? Cheeses, Cigars, Plants

10 In which country were saunas invented? Russia, Finland, Sweden

ANSWERS

1. Dallas 2. Rugby Union 3. Tobermory 4. Venus 5. Lennon 6. Isle Of Man
7. Wales 8. Champion 9. Cigars 10. Finland

QUIZ 31

1 Goulash is the national dish of which country?
   Jamaica, Hungary, Kenya

2 What is the alternative name for a zucchini?
   Pumpkin, Courgette, Leek

3 James Intermediate and Autumn King are both
   varieties of which vegetable?   Pea, Onion, Carrot

4 In which county did Cheddar cheese originate?
   Cheshire, Somerset, Yorkshire

5 What provides the staple diet of koala bears?
   Bamboo shoots, Honey, Eucalyptus leaves

6 On brandy bottles what does the P stand for in
   the abbreviation VSOP?   Port, Paris, Pale

7 What accompanies bacon in the dish Angels on
   Horseback?   Oysters, Prunes, Aubergines

8 What is Zinfandel a variety of?   Pear, Marrow, Wine

9 Which soup features in the title of a 1975 hit for
   10CC?   Tomato, Gazpacho, Minestrone

10 What nuts are used to flavour marzipan?
    Hazelnut, Almond, Peanuts

ANSWERS

1. Hungary 2. Courgette 3. Carrot 4. Somerset 5. Eucalyptus leaves 6. Pale
7. Oysters 8. Wine 9. Minestrone 10. Almond

QUIZ 32

1. Which nursery rhyme character sat among the cinders? Molly Hinders, Polly Flinders, Holly Winders

2. How many Presidents of the USA preceded George W Bush Jnr? 42, 43, 48

3. Bobbin and needlepoint are both types of what? Moth, Lace, Snail

4. In which US state is the city of Reno, famed for its quickie divorces? Texas, Nevada, Alabama

5. What is Ted Danson's profession in the US sitcom *Becker*? Doctor, Lawyer, Teacher

6. What is the second most highly populated city in Austria? Salzburg, Graz, Linz

7. In which country did Ariel Sharon win a 2003 General Election? Lithuania, Jordan, Israel

8. What is the name of the orang-utan in the film *Every Which Way But Loose*? Louie, Clyde, Bonzo

9. In which ocean is the island of Newfoundland? Arctic, Atlantic, Indian

10. In which 1976 film did Walter Matthau play a baseball coach? *Bad News Bears*, *Bad News Bulls*, *Bad News Birds*

ANSWERS

1. Polly Flinders 2. 42 3. Lace 4. Nevada 5. Doctor 6. Graz 7. Israel
8. Clyde 9. Atlantic 10. *Bad News Bears*

QUIZ 33

1 Which fish family does the herring belong to?
Anchovy, Shark, Bass

2 What bird provides the official state nickname of
Louisiana? Eagle, Falcon, Pelican

3 What dance is also the collective noun for a group
of rattlesnakes? Mamba, Rumba, Twist

4 What is the alternative name for a marmot?
Gerbil, Prairie dog, Bobcat,

5 The adjective cervine refers to which animal?
Crocodile, Rabbit, Deer

6 What name is given to a male fox? Bull, Tom, Dog

7 Blue and Seal point are both varieties of which
cat? Burmese, Siamese, Persian,

8 La vaca is the Spanish for what? Cow, Horse, Pig

9 From which South American country did
Paddington Bear travel to Britain? Bolivia,
Argentina, Peru

10 What is a marmoset? Bird, Monkey, Wild dog

ANSWERS

QUIZ 34

1 What bird has the name of a murder suspect in the board game Cluedo?   Peacock, Parrot, Puffin

2 What does a lepidopterist study? Butterflies, Diseases, Languages

3 William Wallace, the subject of the film *Braveheart* died in which century?   14th, 15th, 16th

4 Which British newspaper has a clock on its front page depicting the time of 4.30?   *The Times*, *The Guardian*, *The Mirror*

5 Which city stands at the confluence of the rivers Danube and Sava?   Belgrade, Vienna, Berlin

6 Who created the literary character of Biggles? WE Johns, WE Davids, WE Phillips

7 Which canal bypasses Niagara Falls?   Nelson Canal, Welland Canal, Union Canal

8 Which car manufacturer has made models called Riva and the Cossack?   Lada, Ford, Skoda

9 Which US President penned an autobiography entitled, Where's The Rest Of Me?   Bill Clinton, Ronald Reagan, Gerald Ford

10 From which club did Manchester United FC sign Rio Ferdinand? Luton Town, Leeds United, Arsenal

ANSWERS

1. Peacock 2. Butterflies 3. 14th 4. *The Times* 5. Belgrade 6. WE Johns
7. Welland Canal 8. Lada 9. Ronald Reagan 10. Leeds United

QUIZ 35

• •

1 Which country has a name meaning, Land of Silver?   Sierra Leone, Argentina, Costa Rica

2 What is Canada's oldest city?   Quebec, Ottawa, Toronto

3 Which country is linked to Italy by the Brenner Pass?   Austria, France, Andorra

4 Cape Horn lies at the southern tip of which continent?   North America, South America, Africa

5 By what name is Mount Godwin Austen otherwise known?   Eiger, Mont Blanc, K2

6 Which country is home to the volcano Krakotoa? Taiwan, Indonesia, Japan

7 In which Swiss city are the headquarters of the Red Cross?   Geneva, Basle, Zurich

8 In which country does the River Amazon empty into the sea?   Venezuela, Brazil, Chile

9 What is the capital of Tenerife?   Santa Fe, Santa Cruz, Santa Ana

10 On which river does the city of Montreal stand? St Lawrence, Missouri, Mississippi

ANSWERS

QUIZ 36

• •

1   What unit of electrical capacitance was named after Michael Faraday?   Farad, Arad, Aday

2   What is the nickname of the city of Chicago? Rainy City, Windy City, Foggy City

3   Who did Christopher Lloyd voice in the animated film *Anastasia*?   Lenin, Rasputin, Nicholas II

4   On which island does Jim Bergerac bring criminals to justice?   Ibiza, Jersey, Sark

5   What was the Holy Grail?   Book, Cup, Bones

6   What mode of transport connects the films *The Hunt For Red October* and *Crimson Tide*? Battleship, Submarine, Jet

7   How many children did Adam and Eve have? Two, Three, Nine

8   Who plays the mother of Victoria Wood in the TV comedy *Dinnerladies*?   Julie Walters, June Whitfield, Anne Reid

9   What is the name of the highest waterfall in the USA?   Boulder Falls, Yosemite Falls, Niagara Falls

10 In which state of Australia is Sydney located? Western Australia, New South Wales, Queensland

ANSWERS

1. Farad 2. Windy City 3. Rasputin 4. Jersey 5. Cup 6. Submarine 7. Three
8. Julie Walters 9. Yosemite Falls 10. New South Wales

QUIZ 37

1 Of which city is the TV personality Jerry Springer a former mayor? Springfield, Chicago, Cincinatti

2 Who was the first British woman to travel in space? Helen Sharman, Sally Ryde, Janet Reno

3 In what decade did the author DH Lawrence die? 1920s, 1930s, 1960s

4 Who has airports named after him in Venezuela and Ecuador? Diego Maradona, Simon Bolivar, Fidel Castro,

5 How many children did Queen Victoria have? Nine, Eleven, Fifteen

6 Excluding monarchs, who was the first woman to feature on a British bank note? Enid Blyton, Florence Nightingale, Amy Johnson

7 What post did Andrew Motion take in 1999? Poet Laureate, Astronomer Royal, Archbishop Of York

8 Who succeeded Gerald Ford as President of the USA? Bill Clinton, Jimmy Carter, Ronald Reagan,

9 Which actor was born Harvey Lee Yeary? Lee J Cobb, Lee Majors, Bruce Lee,

10 In what year was the singer Robbie Williams born? 1972, 1974, 1976

ANSWERS

1. Cincinatti 2. Helen Sharman 3. 1930s 4. Simon Bolivar 5. Nine
6. Florence Nightingale 7. Poet Laureate 8. Jimmy Carter 9. Lee Majors
10. 1974

QUIZ 38

• •

1 What is a vibraphone?   Hearing aid, Mobile phone, Musical instrument

2 Which Dickens novel features the character of Jacob Marley?   *Oliver Twist*, *A Christmas Carol*, *David Copperfield*

3 What is a sarcophagus?   Dinosaur, Muscle, Coffin

4 Which US state is known as, The Heart of Dixie? Arizona, Alabama, Texas

5 Which George was born Eric Blair?   George Formby, George Hamilton, George Orwell

6 Which car manufacturer made its Formula One debut at the 2002 Australian Grand Prix?   Jaguar, Toyota, Lexus

7 Which London landmark was built in memory of the victories of Horatio Nelson?   Big Ben, Marble Arch, Lambeth Palace

8 What is the collective noun for a group of magpies?   Steal, Tiding, Theft

9 Which inspector solved the crime in the novel *Service Of All The Dead*?   Wexford, Maigret, Morse

10 The Queen Alexandra Birdwing is the world's largest species of what?   Butterfly, Bat, Moth

ANSWERS

1. Musical instrument 2. *A Christmas Carol* 3. Coffin 4. Alabama 5. George Orwell 6. Toyota 7. Marble Arch 8. Tiding 9. Inspector Morse 10. Butterfly

QUIZ 39

1. Which canal links the North Sea to the Baltic Sea? Gota, Union, Kiel

2. In which ocean does the Benguela current flow? Atlantic, Arctic, Indian

3. Which English football club plays at the Riverside Stadium? Fulham, Stoke City, Middlesbrough

4. The River Jordan empties into which sea? Sea of Galilee, Dead Sea, Black Sea

5. What is the longest river in Europe? Volga, Rhine, Danube

6. What is the largest country that the River Nile flows through? Uganda, Egypt, Sudan

7. In which country is the delta of the River Ganges located? Afghanistan, Bangladesh, India,

8. How many gold medals did the swimmer Mark Spitz win at the 1972 Summer Olympics? 6, 7, 8

9. Yokohama is the seaport of which city? Kuala Lumpur, Nagasaki, Tokyo

10. Which female singer had a 1981 top twenty hit with the song 'Water On Glass'? Suzi Quatro, Kim Wilde, Hazel O'Connor

ANSWERS

1. Kiel Canal 2. Indian Ocean 3. Middlesbrough 4. Dead Sea 5. Volga
6. Sudan 7. Bangladesh 8. Seven 9. Tokyo 10. Kim Wilde

QUIZ 40

1 What name is given to the number in the bottom half of a fraction? Numerator, Escalator, Denominator

2 What genre of novels does Zane Grey write? Westerns, Romance, Horror

3 In what month is the official birthday of Queen Elizabeth II? April, June, December

4 British policemen were named Peelers in honour of whom? Emma Peel, John Peel, Robert Peel

5 In which sport was Fred Perry crowned world champion in 1929? Pool, Table tennis, Darts

6 Who wrote the novel *Little Women*? Jane Austen, Louisa May Alcott, Emily Bronte

7 What name is given to a matador on horseback? Stevedore, Picador, Isadore

8 *When Nature Calls* is the sub-title of which film sequel? *Born Free*, *Ace Ventura*, *Jungle Book*

9 Which football league club did Joe Royle manage in the 2003/04 season? Norwich City, Crystal Palace, Ipswich Town

10 In 1997, Hungary and Poland became members of which organisation? FIFA, OPEC, NATO

ANSWERS

1. Denominator 2. Westerns 3. April 4. Robert Peel 5. Table tennis
6. Louisa May Alcott 7. Picador 8. *Ace Ventura* 9. Ipswich Town 10. NATO

QUIZ 41

• •

1 What does the C stand for in UNESCO? Country, Charity, Cultural

2 What does the A stand for in DNA? Amino, Acid, Alkali

3 What does the C stand for in YMCA? Church, Christian, Campus

4 What do the initials APT stand for with regard to transport? All Points Tram, Automated Power Tricycle, Allow Police Traffic,

5 What does the T stand for in the acronym SWAT? Tactics, Training, Target -

6 What does the A stand for in NATO? American, Army, Atlantic

7 What sport is governed by the IRF? Rowing, Racketball, Rugby

8 What does the O signify with regard to the P & O steamship company? Oil, Oceanic, Oriental

9 What does the M stand for in the cricket organisation MCC? Marylebone, Middlesex, Members

10 With regard to the economic world what do the initials ERM stand for? Europes Reserve Money, Equal Retail Market, Exchange Rate Mechanism

ANSWERS

1. Cultural 2. Acid 3. Christian 4. Advanced Passenger Train 5. Tactics
6. Atlantic 7. Racketball 8. Oriental 9. Marylebone 10. Exchange Rate
Mechanism

QUIZ 42

. . . .

1 Which organisation's vow of silence is known as the Omerta? IRA, Mafia, SAS

2 Where in the human body is the tarsal joint? Hip, Ankle, Elbow

3 What is the hometown of The Simpsons? Springfield, Colorado Springs, Sunnydale

4 Mickle Fell is the highest point of which English county? Devon, Dorset, Durham

5 In which Australian state are the Blue Mountains? Victoria, Queensland, New South Wales

6 Who was the first John to be crowned Snooker World Champion? John Spencer, John Pulman, John Parrott

7 From which language did the word Amen originate? Hebrew, German, Spanish

8 What creature has a name that means, man of the woods? Gorilla, Orang-utan, Yeti,

9 What does the B stand for in the name of the car manufacturer BMW? Black, Bonn, Bavarian

10 In which century was William the Conqueror crowned King of England? 11th, 12th, 13th

ANSWERS

1. Mafia 2. Ankle 3. Springfield 4. Durham 5. New South Wales
6. John Pulman 7. Hebrew 8. Orang-utan 9. Bavarian 10. 11th

QUIZ 43

• •

1 In which city was the first *Die Hard* film set? New York, Los Angeles, Chicago

2 Who was the only British actor to win a Best Actor Oscar in the 1980s? John Hurt, Ben Kingsley, Bob Hoskins

3 What is Bill Murray's job in the film *Groundhog Day*? Vet, Fireman, Weatherman

4 Who played the role of Big Chris Sting in the film *Lock, Stock And Two Smoking Barrels*? Vinnie Jones, Mike Reid, Guy Ritchie

5 Who directed the film *The Deer Hunter*? Michael Cimono, Martin Scorsese, Tobe Hooper

6 Which teenager won a 2001 Best Actor BAFTA? Macaulay Culkin, Anna Paquin, Jamie Bell

7 In which war was the film *Born On The Fourth Of July* set? Vietnam War, Korean War, US Civil War

8 Which sport features in the film *Seabiscuit*? Swimming, Horse racing, Yachting

9 Which character is voiced by Brian Blessed in the *Star Wars* films? Boss Nass, Darth Maul, C-3PO

10 In which film did Clint Eastwood kill David Soul? *Magnum Force, Tightrope, The Rookie*

ANSWERS

1. Los Angeles 2. Ben Kingsley 3. Weatherman 4. Vinnie Jones 5. Michael Cimono 6. Jamie Bell 7. Vietnam War, 8. Horse racing 9. Boss Nass 10. *Magnum Force*

QUIZ 44

1 What is the smallest planet in the Solar System?
   Earth, Pluto, Mercury

2 What is known as The Old Lady Of Threadneedle
   Street? Big Ben, Bank Of England, Globe Theatre

3 Despite singing Stand By Your Man, how many
   times was Tammy Wynette married? 4, 5, 6

4 In which country did Pernod originate? China,
   Canada, France

5 Which series of films features the character of
   police detective Martin Riggs? *Lethal Weapon,
   The Pink Panther, Naked Gun*

6 Which organ of the body stores the bile produced
   by the liver? Kidney, Gall bladder, Spleen

7 Which British daily newspaper has a crusader as
   its logo? *Daily Mail, Daily Star, Daily Express*

8 What is the first name of Costello in the comedy
   duo Abbott & Costello? Bing, Lou, Elvis

9 What is the nationality of former tennis star Pat
   Cash? South African, Canadian, Australian

10 The cities of Gothenburg and Malmo are located
   in which country? Sweden, Germany, Iceland

ANSWERS

1. Pluto 2. Bank Of England 3. 5 4. France 5. *Lethal Weapon* 6. Gall bladder
7. *Daily Express* 8. Lou 9. Australian 10. Sweden

QUIZ 45

1 On which English racecourse is the 1000 Guineas contested? Doncaster, Epsom, Newmarket

2 In which sport did Prince William represent Scotland Universities in 2004? Rugby union, Water Polo, Marathon

3 In which English county is the Brooklands motor racing circuit? Essex, Hampshire, Surrey

4 What nickname was given to the boxer of yesteryear Primo Carnera? Ambling Alp, Man Mountain, Killer Man Jaro

5 Which country hosted the Commonwealth Games in 1930, 1954, 1978 and 1994? Australia, Scotland, Canada

6 How old was Tiger Woods when he won his first US Masters? 19, 21, 22

7 In which sport is the Sheffield Cup contested? Cricket, Polo, Rowing

8 Which US city's American football team is known as The Colts? Kansas, Baltimore, Chicago

9 From what wood are baseball bats traditionally made? Beech, Ash, Willow

10 Who became Snooker World Champion in 2004? Peter Ebdon, Ronnie O'Sullivan, Stephen Hendry

ANSWERS

1. Newmarket 2. Water Polo 3. Surrey 4. Ambling Alp 5. Canada 6. 21
7. Cricket 8. Baltimore 9. Ash 10. Ronnie O'Sullivan

QUIZ 46

1 Who was British Prime Minister at the end of World War I? Herbert Asquith, David Lloyd George, Stanley Baldwin

2 Which group's fourth album is entitled Standing On The Shoulders Of Giants? Blur, Oasis, The Corrs

3 In which town is William Shakespeare buried? Penzance, Torquay, Stratford-Upon-Avon

4 What is the name of the home ground of Celtic Football Club? Easter Road, Parkhead, Ibrox Park,

5 What is made of potassium nitrate, sulphur and charcoal? Tobacco, Talcum powder, Gunpowder

6 Which Formula One Grand Prix is contested at Imola? Monte Carlo, Japanese, San Marino

7 Who won a Best Actor award at the 2003 BAFTAs? Russell Crowe, Kevin Spacey, Daniel Day Lewis

8 By what name is Rebecca Rolfe better known? Pocahontas, Anastasia, Annie Oakley

9 In 1870 which Irishman founded his first home for homeless boys? Dr Knox, Dr Foster, Dr Barnardo

10 From which plant is digitalis obtained? Deadly nightshade, Foxglove, Poppy

ANSWERS

QUIZ 47

• •

1 The first episode of which TV series was entitled, *If I Were A Carpenter*? *Auf Wiedersehen Pet*, *Minder*, *Boys From The Blackstuff*

2 Which organisation does Captain Scarlet work for? Spectrum International Rescue, World Intelligence Network, Nemesis

3 Which characters speak the language of Oddle Poddle? Bill and Ben, The Tweenies, Pinky & Perky

4 Which TV series is set at Gasforth Police Station? *The Thin Blue Line*, *Juliet Bravo*, *The Gentle Touch*

5 What type of animal is Dylan in *The Magic Roundabout*? Rabbit, Snail, Dog

6 Which character was played by Christopher Ryan in *The Young Ones*? Mike, Neil, Rik

7 Who captained the Trumpton firemen? Captain Flack, Captain Jack, Captain Black

8 In which century was the martial arts drama *The Water Margin* set? 12th, 14th, 16th

9 What race is Lieutenant Worf in *Star Trek:The Next Generation*? Klingon, Human, Romulan

10 What is the name of the central family in the comedy series *Bread*? Boswell, Davis, Pringle

ANSWERS

1. *Auf Wiedersehen Pet* 2. Spectrum International Rescue 3. Bill and Ben
4. *The Thin Blue Line* 5. Rabbit 6. Mike 7. Captain Flack 8. 14th 9. Klingon
10. Boswell

QUIZ 48

1 If a person is suffering from hypertrichosis, they possess an abnormal amount of what? Teeth, Hair, Muscles

2 What does 'algia' signify? Plant, Pain, Gold

3 Which country is the nearest neighbour to Greenland? Denmark, Finland, Canada

4 Which pop group were Rocking All Over The World in 1977? Slade, T Rex, Status Quo

5 What was the capital of Italy between 1861 and 1864? Vatican City, Turin, Naples

6 What name is given to the calcified tissue of a tooth? Plaque, Enamel, Dentine

7 What is the ultimate Court of Appeal in the United Kingdom? House of Lords, House of Commons, The Old Bailey

8 In which building is King George II buried? Westminster Abbey, St Paul's Cathedral, Canterbury Cathedral

9 What number of Pennsylvania Avenue is the White House's address? 1200, 1400, 1600

10 On which island is the novel *Anne Of Green Gables* set? Prince Edward Island, Prince Charles Island, Prince Andrew Island

ANSWERS

1. Hair 2. Pain 3. Canada 4. Status Quo 5. Turin 6. Dentine 7. House of Lords 8. Westminster Abbey 9. 1600 10. Prince Edward Island

QUIZ 49

• •

In which countries were the following people born?

1 Bruce Willis   Germany, USA, Scotland

2 Sid James   2, South Africa, Turkey, Argentina

3 Vaness Mae   Japan, Singapore, Malaysia

4 Yul Brynner   Bulgaria, Kenya, Russia

5 Sam Neill   Mexico, New Zealand, Australia

6 Spike Milligan   Ireland, India, Indonesia

7 Harry Houdini   Denmark, Hungary, France

8 Nicole Kidman   Australia, England, USA

9 Pablo Picasso   Spain, Italy, Andorra

10 Marie Curie   Czechoslovakia, Poland, Austria

ANSWERS

1. Germany 2. South Africa 3. Singapore 4. Russia 5. New Zealand 6. India
7. Hungary 8. USA 9. Spain 10. Poland

QUIZ 50

. . . .

1 The Beaufort Sea is part of which ocean? Indian, Pacific, Arctic

2 Charon is the only moon of which planet? Venus, Neptune, Pluto

3 What do animals described as ungulate possess? Webbed feet, Hooves, Horns

4 For what crime was Al Capone imprisoned in 1931? Tax evasion, Blackmail, Bootlegging

5 Which European capital city stands on the River Senne? Copenhagen, Brussels, Paris

6 Which Bond villain has been played by several actors including Telly Savalas? Dr No, Blofeld, Largo

7 In which British city is the Millennium Stadium? London, Birmingham, Cardiff

8 Which was the first German city to host the Summer Olympics? Bonn, Munich, Berlin

9 What does an oenologist drink? Whisky, Wine, Milk

10 What is the official language of Andorra? Catalan, Italian, Portuguese

ANSWERS

1. Arctic 2. Pluto 3. Hooves 4. Tax evasion 5. Brussels 6. Blofeld 7. Cardiff
8. Berlin 9. Wine 10. Catalan

QUIZ 51

• •

What does the …

1 F stand for in the name of F Scott Fitzgerald?
   Farquaad, Francis, Finlay

2 T stand for in the name of Ian T Botham?
   Terence, Timothy, Tarquin

3 P stand for in the name of PW Botha?   Peregrine,
   Percival, Pieter

4 C stand for in the name of CS Lewis?   Cedric,
   Clive, Christopher

5 H stand for in the name of HG Wells?   Hunter,
   Herbert, Harold

6 O stand for in the name of OJ Simpson?   Oliver,
   Orson, Orenthal

7 E stand for in the name of HE Bates?   Ernest,
   Ethelred, Egbert

8 W stand for in the name of Frank W Woolworth?
   Warren, Winfield, Wilberforce

9 E stand for in the name of William E Gladstone?
   Ellington, Ewart, Everard

10 AA stand for in the name of AA Milne?   Alan
   Alexander, Andrew Alva, Adrian Alfred

ANSWERS

1. Francis 2. Terence 3. Pieter 4. Clive 5. Herbert 6. Orenthal 7. Ernest
8. Winfield 9. Ewart 10. Alan Alexander

QUIZ 52

1 In which TV show did James Bolam play a hospital patient called Figgis? *Dr At Large, Only When I Laugh, Dr In The House*

2 What is the chief language spoken in Algeria? French, Spanish, Arabic

3 What does 'CB' stand for in radio terminology? Car Broadcast, Communication Bay, Citizens Band

4 What is the title of George Michael's greatest hits album? *Boys And Girls, Ladies And Gentlemen, Fathers And Sons*

5 Which king ruled England for the first 35 years of the 1100s? Henry I, Henry II, Stephen I

6 Which underwater vessel was captained by Troy Tempest on TV? Seaview, Nautilus, Stingray

7 In which card game is the Bermuda Bowl contested? Canasta, Bridge, Cribbage

8 In which century was Dick Whittington born? 12th, 14th, 16th

9 What is the nationality of the painter Edvard Munch? Russian, Norwegian, Danish

10 Which TV duo are associated with Huggy Bear? Mork & Mindy, Starsky & Hutch, The Odd Couple

ANSWERS

1. *Only When I Laugh* 2. Arabic 3. Citizens Band 4. *Ladies And Gentlemen*
5. Henry I 6. Stingray 7. Bridge 8. 14th 9. Norwegian 10. Starsky & Hutch

QUIZ 53

1 Which country is home to the Pindus mountain range? Italy, Germany, Greece

2 Flanders is an area in which European country? Netherlands, Belgium, Denmark

3 What is the national flower of Sweden? Edelweiss, Lily of the Valley, Geranium

4 Funchal is the capital of which European island? Malta, Madeira, Tenerife

5 Which country on mainland Europe is closest to the island of Corfu? Albania, Greece, Turkey

6 Which country is home to the European Court of Justice? Hungary, France, Luxembourg

7 Which country was once referred to as The Sick Man of Europe? Bulgaria, Cyprus, Turkey

8 Which European capital is served by Templehof Airport? Warsaw, Vienna, Berlin

9 Which two football teams contested the 2004 European Champions Cup final? Inter Milan and Barcelona, Ajax and Chelsea, Porto and Monaco

10 Which European capital city was devastated by an earthquake in 1755? Lisbon, Helsinki, Athens,

ANSWERS

1. Greece 2. Belgium 3. Lily of the Valley 4. Madeira 5. Albania
6. Luxembourg 7. Turkey 8. Berlin 9. Porto and Monaco 10. Lisbon

QUIZ 54

. . . .

1 Phobos is a moon of which planet? Uranus, Pluto, Mars

2 What is the capital of the island of Alderney? St Anne's, St Mary's, St June's

3 What is a kakapo? A tropical fish, A stringed instrument, A flightless bird

4 What is the name of Hamlet's mother in the Shakespeare play? Gertrude, Gwendoline, Guinevere

5 Which country is called Suomi in its native language? China, Finland, Turkey

6 What bird is the international symbol of happiness? Owl, Bluebird, Dove

7 What is brontophobia the fear of? Thunder, Dinosaurs, Elephants

8 Variola is the technical name for which disease? Chickenpox, Smallpox, Measles

9 What is the plural of scampi? Scampu, Scampis, Scampo

10 Which state of the USA is known as the Sioux State? North Dakota, South Dakota, North Carolina

ANSWERS

1. Mars 2. St Anne's 3. A flightless bird 4. Gertrude 5. Finland 6. Bluebird
7. Thunder 8. Smallpox 9. Scampo 10. North Dakota

QUIZ 55

• •

1 What colour is the murder victim in Cluedo?
   Black, Scarlet, Mustard

2 What did Shakespeare refer to as The green-eyed
   monster?   Greed, Lust, Jealousy

3 What spirit forms the base of a White Russian
   cocktail?   Vodka, Whisky, Gin

4 What colour was the owl and the pussycat's
   sailing vessel?   Sky blue, Pea green, Deep purple

5 What breed of parrot featured in the famed
   Monty Python parrot sketch?   Norwegian Blue,
   Dutch Yellow, Flemish Pink

6 What was the name of Dick Turpin's faithful
   horse?   Black Bess, Red Admiral, Silver Ghost

7 What name is given to the award for the best film
   at the Berlin Film Festival?   Golden Lion, Golden
   Bear, Golden Bowl

8 What colour is the property of Fleet Street on a
   Monopoly board?   Red, Yellow, Green

9 What colour follows red in a rainbow?   Orange,
   Violet, Green

10 Which actor famed for playing a TV cop had a
    number one hit in 1977 with the song 'Silver
    Lady'?   Bruce Willis, Don Johnson, David Soul

ANSWERS

1. Black 2. Jealousy 3. Vodka 4. Pea green 5. Norwegian Blue 6. Black Bess
7. Golden Bear 8. Red 9. Orange 10. David Soul

QUIZ 56

. . . .

1 Which French term literally means bottom of the bag? Pot pourri, A la carte, Cul de sac

2 Which American President founded the Peace Corps? Calvin Coolidge, John F Kennedy, Dwight Eisenhower

3 According to the nursery rhyme, what is Wednesday's Child? Full of Grace, Full of woe, Fair of face

4 Which city is known as the Pearl of the Orient? Beijing, Shanghai, Manila

5 According to the proverb, truth is stranger than what? Fiction, Lies, Fantasy

6 At what age did Buddy Holly die? 22, 24, 26

7 What did God create on the sixth day? Heaven, Man, Stars

8 What flavour of soup was depicted on Andy Warhol's painting of Campbell's soup cans? Vegetable, Chicken, Tomato

9 What title is shared by a 1986 chart topping song for Diana Ross and a film starring Keanu Reeves? 'Chain Reaction', 'Endless Love', 'Surrender'

10 What is Cliff Richard's real first name? Harry, Barry, Gary

ANSWERS

1. Cul de sac 2. John F Kennedy 3. Full of woe 4. Manila 5. Fiction 6. 22
7. Man 8. Tomato 9. 'Chain reaction' 10. Harry

QUIZ 57

1 Which player scored the winning goal in the 1971 FA Cup final?   George Graham, Charlie George, George Best

2 From which club did Manchester United sign Ruud Van Nistelrooy? Brondy, PSV Eindhoven, Ajax

3 Who was named PFA Player of the Year in 2004? Thierry Henry, Michael Owen, Ashley Cole

4 Which club play their home matches at the Hawthorns? Wolverhampton Wanderers, West Bromwich Albion, West Ham United

5 Which country were the beaten finalists in the 1970 soccer World Cup? England, Brazil, Italy

6 Who did Nicholas Anelka play for in the 2003/04 season?   Arsenal, Manchester City, Liverpool

7 Which club was beaten in the 2003 UEFA Cup final?   Celtic, Tottenham Hotspur, Rangers

8 In which city is the Maracana Stadium?   Madrid, Rio de Janeiro, Lisbon

9 Who were the first British club to lose in the final of the European Cup? Newcastle United, Leeds United, Sheffield United

10 What profession provides the nickname of Northampton Town?   Cobblers, Hatters, Bakers

ANSWERS

1. Charlie George 2. PSV Eindhoven 3. Thierry Henry 4. West Bromwich Albion 5. Italy 6. Manchester City 7. Celtic 8. Rio de Janeiro 9. Leeds United 10. Cobblers

QUIZ 58

. . . .

1 What is the capital of the state of Western Australia?   Alice Springs, Darwin, Perth

2 What does the P stand for in the acronym OPEC? Platinum, Petroleum, Paraffin

3 What name is given to a male donkey?   Jack, Tom, Tony

4 What is the name of the memorial gardens to John Lennon in New York's Central Park?   Penny Lane, Strawberry Fields, Sergeant Peppers

5 What is the only mythical creature depicted in the Chinese calendar?   Hydra, Dragon, Gorgon

6 Which tennis star of yesteryear was nicknamed, The Crocodile?   Rene Lacoste, Fred Perry, Don Budge

7 In which month of the year does Trafalgar Day fall?   February, July, October

8 What is the duration of a rugby union match? 80 minutes, 90 minutes, 100 minutes

9 In which country did Lancia cars originate?   Italy, Malaysia, USA

10 Jacko is Australian slang for which bird?   Emu, Kookaburra, Ostrich

ANSWERS

1. Perth 2. Petroleum 3. Jack 4. Strawberry Fields 5. Dragon
6. Rene Lacoste 7. October 8. 80 minutes 9. Italy 10. Kookaburra

QUIZ 59

1 What is the middle name of Fred Elliott in
   Coronation Street? Chopin, Handel, Bach

2 Who joined *Emmerdale* in 2004 as Sadie King?
   Joanna Lumley, Patsy Kensit, Michelle Collins

3 Lauren Carpenter is in which Australian soap?
   Neighbours, *Home And Away*, *The Sullivans*

4 Who played LeeAnn De La Vega in *Dallas*?
   Barbara Eden, Mary Crosby, Lesley Anne Down

5 Which soap set in Massachusetts features the
   Leery family? *Falcon Crest*, *Dawson's Creek*, *As The
   World Turns*

6 Which *Coronation Street* character ran the Golden
   Years dating agency? Alec Gilroy, Mike Baldwin,
   Albert Tatlock

7 What was the nickname of the *EastEnders*
   character George Holloway? Shorty, Stilts, Lofty

8 Who joined *Bad Girls* as wing governor Frances
   Myers? Anita Dobson, Eva Pope, Tina Hobley

9 What is Karl Foster's job in *Coronation Street*?
   Sales rep, Nurse, Mechanic

10 In 2004, which *EastEnders* character revealed that
   he had a secret wife called Chrissie? Dirty Den
   Watts, Nick Cotton, Phil Mitchell

ANSWERS

1. Handel 2. Patsy Kensit 3. *Neighbours* 4. Barbara Eden 5. *Dawson's Creek*
6. Alec Gilroy 7. Lofty 8. Eva Pope 9. Nurse 10. Dirty Den Watts

QUIZ 60

. . . .

1 Where was King Arthur taken to after his death?
Avalon, Jerusalem, Camelot

2 In what month of 1939 did Britain declare war on
Germany? September, April, August

3 What was the name of the space craft in which
Yuri Gagarin made the first historic space flight?
Vostock 1, Sputnik 1, Voyager 1

4 What is the top hand in a game of poker? Royal
Flush, Four of a kind, Full house

5 In which film did Anne Bancroft play Mrs
Robinson? *The Graduate*, *Swiss Family Robinson*,
Lost In Space

6 Who solves the crimes in the *Murder She Wrote*
series? Jessica Fletcher, Miss Marple, Nancy Drew

7 What is the first day of Lent? Ash Wednesday,
Shrove Tuesday, Good Friday

8 What bird did my true love give to me on the
sixth day of Christmas? Geese, Swans, Hens

9 According to Napoleon Boneparte an army
marches on its what? Stomach, Enemies, Feet

10 In which century did Wat Tyler lead the Peasant's
Revolt? 13th, 14th, 17th

ANSWERS

1. Avalon 2. September 3. Vostock 1 4. Royal Flush 5. *The Graduate*
6. Jessica Fletcher 7. Ash Wednesday 8. Geese 9. Stomach 10. 14th

QUIZ 61

● ●

1 Which car manufacturer uses the advertising slogan, "The car in front"? Jaguar, Toyota, Hyundai

2 Which Roman road connected London to York? Watling Street, Ermine Street, New Lane

3 What does the CC stand for in the shipping abbreviation, VLCC? Crude Carrier, Cabin Crew, Continental Cruiser

4 In which country did Volvo cars originate? Russia, USA, Sweden

5 Which British airport was first called Ringway? Heathrow, Manchester, Stansted

6 The Trans-Siberian railway ran from Moscow to which other city? Minsk, Vladisvostock, Leningrad

7 What is the collective noun for a group of camels? Fleet, Train, Caravan

8 In what decade did Thor Heyerdahl cross the Pacific on the Kon-Tiki raft? 1930s, 1940s, 1950s

9 Which billionaire owned a yacht called Talitha G? Aristotle Onassis, John Paul Getty, Robert Maxwell

10 Which city is served by an underground station called The Metropolitania? Naples, Rome, Milan

ANSWERS

1. Toyota 2. Ermine Street 3. Crude Carrier 4. Sweden 5. Manchester
6. Vladisvostocki 7. Caravan 8. 1940s 9. John Paul Getty 10. Rome

QUIZ 62

• •

1 What was the name of the character played by Yul Brynner in *The Magnificent Seven*? Vin, Chicom Chris

2 How many planets in the Solar System are larger than Earth? 3, 4, 5

3 What is the name of Derek and Rodney Trotter's local pub in Only Fools And Horses? The Nags Head, Grey Horse, The Plough

4 What post is held by Mr Timms in the Postman Pat tales? Police Inspector, Mayor, Reverend

5 Which British city has the most canals? Manchester, Liverpool, Birmingham

6 Which US city is known as the Steel City? San Antonio, Pittsburgh, Milwaukee

7 Which James Bond film shares its title with a variety of banana? *Goldfinger*, *Thunderball*, *Goldeneye*

8 What is gymnophobia the morbid fear of? Exercise, Fighting, Nudity

9 Which African country is surrounded on three sides by Senegal? Zaire, Zambia, Gambia

10 What is the nationality of the snooker star Mark Williams? English, Welsh, Scottish

ANSWERS

1. Chris 2. 4 3. The Nags Head 4. Reverend 5. Birmingham 6. Pittsburgh
7. *Goldfinger* 8. Nudity 9. Gambia 10. Welsh

QUIZ 63

• •

Who penned the following autobiographies?

1 *Oh What A Circus* Andrew Lloyd Webber, Tim Rice, David Essex

2 *I Owe Russia $2000* Rudolph Nureyev, Bob Hope, Peter Ustinov

3 *Yes I Can* Sammy Davis Jnr, Frank Sinatra, Peter Lawford

4 *Facing The Music* Fred Astaire & Ginger Rogers, Torvill and Dean, Morecambe and Wise

5 *Little Girl Lost* Kate Moss, Drew Barrymore, Judy Garland

6 *Eye Of The Tiger* Tiger Woods, Frank Bruno, Bruce Lee

7 *Tall, Dark And Gruesome* Christopher Lee, Jeff Goldblum, Martin Johnson

8 *Don't Laugh At Me* Tommy Cooper, Norman Wisdom, Charlie Chaplin

9 *Life Is Too Short* Willie Carson, Ronnie Corbett, Mickey Rooney

10 *Also Known As Shirley* Shirley Temple, Shelley Winters, Shirley Maclaine

ANSWERS

1. Tim Rice 2. Bob Hope 3, Sammy Davis Jnr 4. Torvill and Dean
5. Drew Barrymore 6. Frank Bruno 7. Christopher Lee 8. Norman Wisdom
9. Mickey Rooney 10. Shelley Winters

QUIZ 64

1. What does the K stand for in the name of the author JK Rowling? Kerry, Kathleen, Karen

2. Which cartoon series features the characters of Fancy and Benny the Ball? *Top Cat*, *South Park*, *The Simpsons*

3. What animal provides the symbol of the star sign Capricorn? Ram, Goat, Bull

4. Cherokee and Celeste are both varieties of which fruit? Apricot, Peach, Cherry

5. Accra is the capital of which African country? Sierra Leone, Ghana, Madagascar

6. Who was the first actor to play Frankenstein's monster on film? Peter Lorre, Boris Karloff, Bela Lugosi

7. Which girl's name provides the name of the capital of the Seychelles? Victoria, Elizabeth, Beverley

8. Who provided the voice of Bugs Bunny? Jim Backus, Mel Blanc, Walt Disney

9. What is the appearance of a face described as rugose? Pale, Wrinkled, Bearded

10. Which member of The Simpsons shot Mr Burns? Lisa, Bart, Maggie

ANSWERS

1. Kathleen 2. *Top Cat* 3. Goat 4. Cherry 5. Ghana 6. Boris Karloff
7. Victoria 8. Mel Blanc 9. Wrinkled 10. Maggie

QUIZ 65

• •

1 What is the last book of the Old Testament?
Jonah, Malachi, Joel

2 Who's was the first death to be recorded in The
Bible?   Adam, Abel, Cain

3 What was the first bird that Noah released from
the ark?   Hawk, Raven, Dove

4 Which biblical character married Zipporah?
Joshua, Moses, Solomon

5 How was John the Baptist related to Jesus?
Uncle, Brother, Cousin

6 Which animals ate the biblical character of
Jezebel? Dogs, Lions, Bats

7 How many books of the Bible begin with the
letter J?   12, 22, 32

8 In the book of Exodus, Moses turns the water of
the River Nile into what?   Dust, Blood, Wine

9 Which book of the Bible consists of 150 sacred
poems?   Numbers, Kings, Psalms

10 What is the third book of the Bible?   Genesis,
Levicticus, Job

ANSWERS

1. Malachi 2. Abel 3. Raven 4. Moses 5. Cousin 6. Dogs 7. 12 8. Blood
9. Psalms 10. Levicticus

QUIZ 66

• •

1 What name is given to a female swan?   Cygnet, Pen, Hen

2 What does a chandler make for a living?   Candles, Hats, Pianos

3 Which TV series centred on the activities of the Globelink News Agency?   *Paparazzi*, *Drop The Dead Donkey*, *Hot Metal*

4 In which country did the chihuahua dog originate? Portugal, Mexico, Uruguay

5 What is the national flower of Japan?   Jasmine, Chrysanthemum, Orchid

6 Nell Trent is the leading female character in which Dickens novel?   *A Tale Of Two Cities*, *The Old Curiosity Shop*, *Hard Times*

7 Which Disney animated film is sub-titled, *The Lost Empire*?   *Sleeping Beauty*, *The Little Mermaid*, *Atlantis*

8 What breed of dog is Pluto, the pet pooch of Mickey Mouse?   Labrador, Bloodhound, Poodle

9 What is the collective noun for a group of owls? Wisdom, Parliament, Hoot

10 In which sea does Corfu lie?   Ionian, Red, Aegean

ANSWERS

1. Pen 2. Candles 3. *Drop The Dead Donkey* 4. Mexico 5. Chrysanthemum
6. *The Old Curiosity Shop* 7. *Atlantis* 8. Bloodhound 9. Parliament
10. Ionian

QUIZ 67

• •

1 How many keys are on a standard piano? 66, 77, 88

2 How many bottles of champagne comprise a Methuselah? 8, 12, 20

3 How many masts does a sloop have? 1, 3, 4

4 How many horses completed the course of the 2001 Grand National? 4, 14, 24

5 How many squares on a Rubik's cube never move position? 4, 6, 10

6 How many books comprise the New Testament? 27, 37, 47

7 How many counties are in Northern Ireland? 6, 8, 10

8 How many pieces of silver did Judas receive for betraying Jesus? 15, 30, 50

9 Over how many holes are major golf tournaments held? 54, 72, 90

10 How many legs does a daddy longlegs have? 6, 8, 10

ANSWERS

1.88 2.8 3.1 4.4 5.6 6.27 7.6 8.30 9.72 10.6

QUIZ 68

. . . .

1 What sport is played by the Scottish Claymores?
   Ice hockey, Rugby union, American football

2 How many horses pull a troika?   3, 6, 7

3 Mount Cook is the highest peak in which
   country? New Zealand, Canada, Australia

4 What name is given to a simple catch in the
   game of cricket?   Bully, Baby, Dolly

5 Emma Harte is the central character of which
   novel?   *Wuthering Heights*, *A Woman Of Substance*,
   Emma

6 What does the M stand for in the computer
   acronym CD ROM?   Music, Mass, Memory

7 In which US state is Princeton University?   New
   York, New Jersey, New Hampshire

8 Which unit of measurement derives its name
   from the Arabic for seed?   Carat, Litre, Metre

9 Which capital city is home to the famed Hofburg
   Palace Spanish Riding School?   Paris, Vienna, Rome

10 What does it mean if a meeting is held, sub rosa?
   Outside, Monthly, In secret

ANSWERS

1. American football 2. 3 3. New Zealand 4. Dolly 5. *A Woman Of Substance*
6. Memory 7. New Jersey 8. Carat 9. Vienna 10. In secret

QUIZ 69

1 What would a citizen of Vietnam do with a dong? Eat it, Play it, Spend it

2 In India, what is a dhoti?   Baker, Loincloth, Flute

3 In Japan, what is a futon?   Hat, Bed, Cigar

4 Which Asian city is served by Dum Dum Airport? Tokyo, Calcutta, Bombay

5 Which country was divided by the 38th Parallel in 1945?   Korea, Vietnam, Pakistan

6 What is the national flower of India?   Jasmine, Lotus, Tiger Lily

7 What is the largest island in the Indian Ocean? Sri Lanka, Java, Madagascar

8 What country is connected to Pakistan by the Khyber Pass?   Tibet, Mongolia, Afghanistan

9 In India, what are the Ghats?   Forests, Straits, Mountains

10 What does the Japanese word karaoke literally mean?   Empty music, Empty orchestra, Empty sound

ANSWERS

1. Spend it 2. Loincloth 3. Bed 4. Calcutta 5. Korea 6. Lotus 7. Madagascar
8. Afghanistan 9. Mountains 10. Empty orchestra

QUIZ 70

1 Montego Bay is a popular holiday destination on which island?   Crete, Cuba, Jamaica

2 In the 60s TV series *Batman*, which actor played a villain called Egghead?   Christopher Lee, Vincent Price, Boris Karloff

3 In the zodiac, what type of sign is Leo?   Fire sign, Earth sign, Water sign

4 What does the A stand for in Steven Spielberg's film, *A.I.*?   Animated, Automated, Artificial

5 Where do the Banks family live in the novel *Mary Poppins*?   Cherry Tree Lane, Poppy Lane, Apple Tree Lane

6 What is the first name of Rumpole Of The Bailey?   Hubert, Henry, Horace

7 What is the national currency of India?   Rupee, Rouble, Baht

8 Which state of the USA is known as the Grand Canyon State?   Alaska, Arizona, Utah

9 Who recorded the album A Day At The Races?   King, Queen, Prince

10 Which US President features on a one dollar bill?   George Washington, Abraham Lincoln, Theodore Roosevelt

ANSWERS

1. Jamaica 2. Vincent Price 3. Fire sign 4. Artificial 5. Cherry Tree Lane
6. Horace 7. Rupee 8. Arizona 9. Queen 10. George Washington

QUIZ 71

- -

1 In which city is the musical *Hello Dolly* set?
   London, New York, New Orleans

2 Which literary character inspired the musical *The Man From La Mancha*? The Scarlet Pimpernel, Don Quixote, The Count Of Monte Cristo

3 Which musical features the song 'It's A Hard Knock Life'? *Oliver, Annie, Kiss Me Kate*

4 Which musical is set in Catfish Row? *West Side Story, Fiddler On The Roof, Porgy & Bess*

5 In which film did Gene Kelly sing I Got Rhythm? *Xanadu, Singin' In The Rain, An American In Paris*

6 Who played Bill Benson in the musical *Anything Goes*? Bing Crosby, Bob Hope, Frank Sinatra

7 Which musical features the songs 'I Feel Pretty, Maria' and 'Somewhere'? *The Sound Of Music, A Star Is Born, West Side Story*

8 What is the last name of Tommy in the rock musical, *Tommy*? Wood, Walker, Wayne

9 In which film did Mitzi Gaynor sing I'm Gonna Wash That Man Right Out Of My Hair? *South Pacific, Show Boat, 42nd Street*

10 Who played the title role in the 1958 musical *Gigi*? Julie Andrews, Natalie Wood, Leslie Caron

ANSWERS

1. New York 2. Don Quixote 3. *Annie* 4. *Porgy & Bess* 5. *An American In Paris*
6. Bing Crosby 7. *West Side Story* 8. Walker 9. *South Pacific* 10. Leslie Caron

QUIZ 72

1 Which group had 1960s hits with 'Waterloo Sunset' and 'Sunny Afternoon'?   The Small Faces, The Kinks, The Monkees

2 To which fruit family does the kumquat belong? Melon, Pear, Orange

3 Which ruler of England acquired the nickname of Tumbledown Dick?   Richard III, Richard Cromwell, Richard II

4 In which state of the USA is the city of Detroit located?   California, Michigan, Ohio

5 What was first used at Newmarket race course in 1965?   Photo finish, Starting stalls, Astroturf

6 In 1997 who became the first full time coach to the England rugby union team?   Will Carling, Alex Murphy, Clive Woodward

7 Where is the Sea Of Clouds?   Jupiter, Mars, Moon

8 What does a dish contain if cooked au gratin? Onions, Cheese, Breadcrumbs

9 Mount Marmolada is the highest peak in which range?   Dolomites, Atlas, Pyrenees

10 In which country did Punch and Judy shows originate?   England, USA, Italy

ANSWERS

1. The Kinks 2. Orange 3. Richard Cromwell 4. Michigan 5. Starting stalls
6. Clive Woodward 7. Moon 8. Cheese 9. Dolomites 10. Italy

QUIZ 73

• •

1 What is a Lent Lily more commonly called?
   Daisy, Daffodil, Crocus

2 What name is given to the home of an otter?
   Warren, Holt, Lodge

3 What is an alewife?   Bird, Fish, Reptile

4 To which continent are tigers native?   Africa,
   Asia, South America

5 In which part of a flower is the pollen produced?
   Stamen, Petal, Anther

6 How many teeth does an elephant have?   4, 8, 12

7 What is the more common name for the
   helianthus?   Tiger lily, Sunflower, Marigold

8 To which plant family does the lilac belong?
   Mulberry, Olive, Nightshade

9 What is the shorter name for the wildebeest?
   Ibex, Gnu, Civet

10 The yaffle is a species of which bird?   Owl,
   Pheasant, Woodpecker

ANSWERS

1. Daffodil 2. Holt 3. Fish 4. Asia 5. Anther 6. 4 7. Sunflower 8. Olive
9. Gnu 10. Woodpecker

QUIZ 74

1 What does the C stand for in the trade union acronym TUC? Corporation, Congress, Council

2 Who narrates the Sherlock Holmes stories? Dr Watson, Mrs Hudson, Sherlock Holmes

3 What is the kitten's name in the Disney animation *Pinocchio*? Worthington, Jiminy, Figaro

4 Which kingdom was ruled by Alexander the Great? Sparta, Macedonia, Asia Minor

5 Which was the first British football club to win two European trophies? Aberdeen, Tottenham Hotspur, Manchester United

6 Who played Tina Carlyle in the 1994 film *The Mask*? Holly Hunter, Cher, Cameron Diaz

7 What was Louise Fletcher's job in the film *One Flew Over The Cuckoo's Nest*? Nurse, Teacher, Taxi driver

8 Whose stage name was once Walter Busterkeys? Harry Houdini, Fats Domino, Liberace

9 By what score did England beat West Germany in the final of the 1966 World Cup? 3-1, 4-1, 4-2

10 Who plays Lord Voldemort in *Harry Potter And The Goblet Of Fire*? John Malkovich, Gary Oldman, Terence Stamp

ANSWERS

1. Congress 2. Dr Watson 3. Figaro 4. Macedonia 5. Tottenham Hotspur
6. Cameron Diaz 7. Nurse 8. Liberace 9. 4-2 10. John Malkovich

QUIZ 75

- -

1 What is the better part of valour? Delusion, Discretion, Deceit

2 According to the proverb, what begins at home? Life, Charity, Happiness

3 Procrastination is said to be the thief of what? Beauty, Sleep, Time

4 Napoleon Boneparte described Britain as a nation of what? Sailors, Shopkeepers, Surgeons

5 What did Karl Marx claim was the opium of the people? Education, Politics, Religion

6 According to Aesop, every what has two sides? Page, Truth, Face

7 What do too many cooks spoil? Broth, Banquet, Breakfast

8 Which US President once said, "If you can't convince them, confuse them"? Harry S Truman, Richard Nixon, Ronald Reagan

9 What brings May flowers? Sunny hours, Barnet fairs, April showers

10 According to an old saying a calm sea does not make a what? Safe journey, Skilled sailor, Still soul

ANSWERS

1. Discretion 2. Charity 3. Time 4. Shopkeepers 5. Religion 6. Truth 7. Broth
8. Harry S Truman 9. April showers 10. Skilled sailor

QUIZ 76

1. What was the original title of the novel *Catch 22*? Catch 12, Catch 14, Catch 18

2. Which island was home to the ancient Greek physician Hippocrates? Symi, Kos, Zante

3. In what year did Dolly the sheep become the first cloned mammal? 1997, 1998, 1999

4. Which French phrase means according to the menu? A la carte, Bon appetit, Coup de grace

5. Who played the role of Dermot in *Men Behaving Badly*? Martin Clunes, Harry Enfield, Ben Elton

6. What is the motto of the Salvation Army? Blood and Fire, My Word Is My Bond, Jesus Lives

7. Who was the first President of the USA to receive the Nobel Peace Prize? Abraham Lincoln, Theodore Roosevelt, George Bush Jnr

8. What title was bestowed upon Prince Edward following his wedding? Lord Of The Isles, Duke Of York, Earl of Wessex

9. How many FA Cup finals did George Best play in? None, 3, 6

10. Who duetted with Gene Pitney on the 1989 hit, 'Somethings Gotten Hold Of My Heart'? David Bowie, Boy George, Marc Almond

ANSWERS

1. Catch 18 2. Kos 3. 1997 4. A la carte 5. Harry Enfield 6. Blood and Fire
7. Theodore Roosevelt 8. Earl of Wessex 9. None 10. Marc Almond

QUIZ 77

• •

1 Luanda is the capital of which African country?
   Angola, Congo, Niger

2 Which of the following accurately describes
   Cameroon?   Principality, Republic, Duchy

3 Which country lies to the immediate south of
   Egypt?   South Africa, Zimbabwe, Sudan

4 What is the most highly populated city in Africa?
   Kampala, Nairobi, Cairo

5 What is the capital of Liberia?   Freetown, Abuja,
   Monrovia

6 What is the Namib on the continent of Africa?
   Desert, Mountain range, Jungle

7 What is the most highly populated country in
   Africa?   Uganda, Morocco, Nigeria

8 In which country is the most easterly point of
   mainland Africa?   Algeria, Somalia, Ethiopia

9 What is the national symbol of South Africa?
   Pomegranate, Springbok, Lion

10 What is Africa's highest capital city?   Addis Ababa,
    Tunis, Pretoria

ANSWERS

1. Angola 2. Republic 3. Sudan 4. Cairo 5. Monrovia 6. Desert 7. Nigeria
8. Somalia 9. Springbok 10. Addis Ababa

QUIZ 78

1 Ganymede is the largest moon of which planet?
   Uranus, Jupiter, Neptune

2 Which film earned Michael Douglas his first Best
   Actor Oscar? *Fatal Attraction, Wall Street, Don't Say
   A Word*

3 How many holes does a ten pin bowling ball
   have? None, 2, 3

4 Who did Andrew Motion replace as Poet
   Laureate? Pam Ayres, Ted Hughes, John Betjeman

5 How many Oscars did Silence Of The Lambs win?
   None, 5, 7

6 What provided the filling of Little Jack Horner's
   pie? Meat, Plum, Cheese

7 Which singer/pianist won a Grammy Award for
   the album 52nd Street? Norah Jones, Billy Joel,
   Randy Newman

8 Which song character was "always window
   shopping"? Georgie Girl, Lady Maddona, Angie

9 Which football club moved from The Dell to St
   Mary's Stadium? Fulham, Millwall, Southampton

10 Bramley and Pearmain Pippin are both varieties
    of what? Pear, Apple, Peach

ANSWERS

1. Jupiter 2. *Wall Street* 3. 3 4. Ted Hughes 5. 5 6. Plum 7. Billy Joel
8. Georgie Girl 9. Southampton 10. Apple

QUIZ 79

1 What is glamour model Jordan's real name? Katie Price, Anna Prince, Kate Peach

2 What anniversary did BBC 2 celebrate in 2004? 30th, 40th, 50th

3 Who was voted Young PFA Player Of The Year in 2004? Wes Brown, Craig Bellamy, Scott Parker

4 Who signed a two year contract with ITV in 2004, after 33 years with the BBC? Michael Parkinson, Barry Norman, Bruce Forsythe

5 Which classic horse race was won by Haafhd in May 2004? 2000 Guineas, The Oaks, The Derby

6 Which English football club were kocked out of the UEFA Cup semi-final in May 2004? Liverpool, Newcastle United, Leeds United

7 Which nation won the Eurovision Song Contest in 2004? Russia, Ukraine, Spain

8 Which TV series ended in 2004 with an episode entitled *The Last One*? *Frasier*, *Friends*, *The X Files*

9 Which annual British sporting event was 150 years old in 2004? Wimbledon, Oxford & Cambridge Boat Race, Grand National

10 What is Gwyneth Paltrow's daughter, born in 2004, named? Cherry, Clementine, Apple

ANSWERS

1. Katie Price 2. 40th 3. Scott Parker 4. Michael Parkinson
5. 2000 Guineas 6. Newcastle United 7. Ukraine 8. *Friends*
9. Oxford & Cambridge Boat Race 10. Apple

QUIZ 80

- -

1 Fromage is the French word for what? Bread, Chocolate, Cheese

2 Who composed the William Tell Overture? Bach, Rossini, Verdi

3 In 1971, Idi Amin became the leader of which country? Saudi Arabia, Uganda, Nigeria

4 Hippophobia is the morbid fear of what? Horses, Hippos, Pigs

5 Which football club lifted England's Premiership trophy in the 2003/04 season? Everton, Chelsea, Arsenal

6 What is the motto of the Boy Scouts? Be Prepared, Who Dares Wins, Duty Calls

7 Who directed the *Death Wish* series of films? Sam Peckinpah, Michael Winner, Alan Parker

8 In which country is the city of Kabul? Algeria, Indonesia, Afghanistan

9 What was Elliott Gould's nickname in the big screen version of MASH? Hawkeye, Radar, Trapper

10 Which jubilee did Queen Elizabeth II celebrate in 1977? Sapphire, Silver, Ruby,

ANSWERS

1. Cheese 2. Rossini 3. Uganda 4. Horses 5. Arsenal 6. Be Prepared
7. Michael Winner 8. Afghanistan 9. Trapper 10. Silver

QUIZ 81

Who said?

1. "Forgive your enemies, but never forget their names"? Nixon, Kennedy, Bush Snr

2. "In the future everyone will be famous for fifteen minutes"? Andy Warhol, Nostradamus, HG Wells

3. "You cannot make a revolution with silk gloves"? Lenin, Stalin, Hitler

4. "We're more popular than Jesus"? John Lennon, Paul McCartney, Ringo Starr

5. "Reports of my death have been greatly exaggerated"? Dickens, Mark Twain, Jules Verne

6. "Those that fail to learn from history, are doomed to repeat it"? Henry VIII, Gandhi, Churchill

7. "England expects that every man will do his duty"? Wellington, Horatio Nelson, Elizabeth I

8. "False facts are highly injurious to the progress of science"? Jenner, Einstein, Darwin

9. "I don't know anything about music. In my line of work you don't have to"? Mick Jagger, Elvis Presley, Andrew Lloyd Webber

10. "A woman is as young as her knees"? Twiggy, Mary Quant, Jackie Kennedy

ANSWERS

1. Kennedy 2. Andy Warhol 3. Stalin 4. John Lennon 5. Mark Twain
6. Winston Churchill 7. Horatio Nelson 8. Darwin 9. Elvis Presley
10. Mary Quant

QUIZ 82

• •

1 Which Rocky film was introduced by the song, 'Eye Of The Tiger'?   *Rocky II, Rocky III, Rocky IV*

2 Which insect is responsible for the spread of malaria?   Hornet, Mosquito, Wasp

3 Who succeeded Queen Victoria on the British throne?   Edward VII, George V, Edward VIII

4 What total is obtained from adding one dozen to a Baker's dozen?   23, 25, 29

5 What type of flower is depicted on the badge of Boy Scouts?   Daffodil, Fleur-de-lys, Heather

6 Who plays the role of Mr Olivander in the *Harry Potter* films?   Ian Holm, John Hurt, John Cleese

7 What name is given to goods washed overboard from a ship?   Ballast, Flotsam, Jetsam

8 In which country were the 1992 Summer Olympic Games held?   Korea, USA, Spain

9 In English history what was danegeld?   A tax, A jousting tournament, A farming community

10 Montgomery is the state capital of which state of the USA?   Delaware, Nebraska, Alabama

ANSWERS

1. *Rocky III* 2. Mosquito 3. Edward VII 4. 25 5. Fleur-de-lys 6. John Hurt
7. Flotsam 8. Spain 9. A tax 10. Alabama

QUIZ 83

• •

In which film did …

1 Meryl Streep play Madeline Ashton? *The Hours,
   The River Wild, Death Becomes Her*

2 Al Pacino play Mayor John Pappas? *Heat, City
   Hall, Any Given Sunday*

3 Harrison Ford play Rick Deckard? *Blade Runner,
   The Fugitive, The Empire Strikes Back*

4 Humphrey Bogart play Charlie Allnut? *Key Largo,
   The Maltese Falcon, The African Queen*

5 Daryl Hannah play Elle Driver? *Steel Magnolias,
   Splash, Kill Bill*

6 Orlando Bloom play Will Turner? *Black Hawk
   Down, Pirates Of The Caribbean, The Calcium Kid*

7 Denzel Washington play Alonzo Harris? *The Bone
   Collector, Training Day, Philadelphia*

8 Jennifer Lopez play Maria Fiore? *Out Of Sight, The
   Wedding Planner, Maid In Manhattan*

9 Burt Reynolds play JJ McClure? *Switching
   Channels, City Heat, The Cannonball Run*

10 Elizabeth Taylor play Pearl Slaghoople? *The
   Comedians, Butterfield 8, The Flintstones*

ANSWERS

1. *Death Becomes Her* 2. *City Hall* 3. *Blade Runner* 4. *The African Queen*
5. *Kill Bill* 6. *Pirates Of The Caribbean* 7. *Training Day* 8. *The Wedding Planner*
9. *The Cannonball Run* 10. *The Flintstones*

QUIZ 84

. . . .

1 Which comedian penned Popcorn and Gridlock?
   Ben Elton, Stephen Fry, John Cleese

2 In the animal kingdom, what is a leatherback?
   Turtle, Cow, Alligator

3 At which school are pupils known as Bluecoats?
   Eton, Charterhouse, Harrow

4 In The Simpsons, what colour is Marge Simpson's
   hair?   Blue, Grey, Red

5 Which film introduced the all action character of
   John Rambo?   *Commando*, *No Mercy*, *First Blood*

6 What type of farm animal is a Romney Suffolk?
   Pig, Duck, Sheep

7 On which island were the Tamil Tigers guerilla
   group founded?   Sri Lanka, Cuba, Cyprus

8 Who did Miranda Richardson portray in the TV
   comedy *Blackadder II*?   Elizabeth I, Catherine Parr,
   Florence Nightingale

9 Which country do the Galapagos Islands belong
   to?   Ecuador, USA, Greenland

10 What name is given to the ring in which a sumo
    wrestling bout takes place?   Gojo, Dojo, Bojo

ANSWERS

1. Ben Elton 2. Turtle 3. Charterhouse 4. Blue 5. *First Blood* 6. Sheep
7. Sri Lanka 8. Elizabeth I 9. Ecuador 10. Dojo

QUIZ 85

1 What is the unusual middle name of the actor Richard Gere?   Paradine, Tiffany, Nesta

2 What surname was Malcolm X born with?   Little, Small, Short

3 Who was born Julia Elizabeth Wells?   Julie Christie, Julie London, Julie Andrews

4 What was the name of Orville Wright's brother?   Wilbur, Ian, Edward

5 What vegetable provides the nickname of the state of Idaho?   Potato, Parsnip, Carrot

6 What surname was shared by the 9th and the 23rd Presidents of the USA?   Wilson, Harrison, Adams

7 What is the last name of the man who invented the cylinder lock?   Keys, Yale, Locke

8 What is the first name of the man after whom Baffin Island is named?   Peter, William, Charles

9 What was the first name of General Custer?   George, David, William

10 What was the last name of the man who invented the battery?   Watt, Volta, Battersby

ANSWERS

1. Tiffany 2. Little 3. Julie Andrews 4. Wilbur 5. Potato 6. Harrison 7. Yale
8. William 9. George 10. Volta

QUIZ 86

1 Which sailing vessel's crew disappeared without trace in 1872? The Flying Dutchman, Mary Rose, Marie Celeste

2 In the game of charades, what is signified by tugging one's ear lobe? Song, Sounds like, Wrong answer

3 In which ocean do the Maldives lie? Atlantic, Arctic, Indian

4 Which film earned Burt Lancaster his only Best Actor Oscar? *Elmer Gantry*, *From Here To Eternity*, *Trapeze*

5 Who created the literary character of Moll Flanders? Dickens, Daniel Defoe, Mark Twain

6 What title provides the nickname of the boxer Naseem Hamed? Duke, Prince, King

7 On how many properties can hotels be built in the game of Monopoly? 18, 20, 22

8 In what year did man first reach the North Pole? 1909, 1919, 1929

9 What common name for a pet dog is derived from the Latin for I trust? Fido, Butch, Rex

10 In the game of Scrabble, two letters have a 10 point value. One is Z, what is the other? J, Q, X

ANSWERS

1. Marie Celeste 2. Sounds like 3. Indian 4. *Elmer Gantry* 5. Daniel Defoe
6. Prince 7. 22 8. 1909 9. Fido 10. Q

QUIZ 87

• •

1 What was Alfred Hitchcock's first colour film?
   Vertigo, Rope, The Birds

2 Who was the first Paul to top the UK singles
   charts?   Paul Anka, Paul Young, Paul McCartney

3 Who was the first goalkeeper to win 100 caps for
   England?   Frank Swift, Gordon Banks, Peter Shilton

4 Who was the first person to get drunk in the
   Bible?   Noah, Cain, Herod

5 What was the title of the first number one hit for
   Take That?   'Never Forget', 'Back For Good', 'Pray'

6 What is the first name of the character played by
   Lee Majors in *The Six Million Dollar Man*?
   Hannibal, Steve, Buck

7 What was the first *Carry On* film?   *Carry On Nurse,
   Carry On Cowboy, Carry On Sergeant*

8 Who was the first Scottish footballer to be voted
   European Footballer Of The Year?   Kenny Dalglish,
   Denis Law, Alan Hansen

9 All Things Must Pass was the first solo album for
   which Beatle?   Paul, George, Ringo

10 Which country hosted the first Commonwealth
    Games?   New Zealand, Canada, Australia

ANSWERS

1. *Rope* 2. Paul Anka 3. Peter Shilton 4. Noah 5. 'Pray' 6. Steve 7. *Carry On
Sergeant* 8. Denis Law 9. George 10. Canada

QUIZ 88

• •

1 What is the birthstone for May? Emerald, Ruby, Sapphire

2 What was the title of the sequel to the TV comedy series *The Golden Girls*? *The Golden Fortress*, *The Golden Palace*, *The Golden Gate*

3 What is the name of the largest loch in Scotland? Loch Neigh, Loch Ness, Loch Lomond

4 What did the Sandwich Islands become? Hawaii, Bahamas, Fiji

5 Which of the following is a dog's name in the *Harry Potter* novels? Hedwig, Scabbers, Fluffy

6 Where in the human body are the muscles known as the lumbricals? Head, Legs, Hand

7 What does the Latin phrase Compos mentis mean? Let the buyer beware, Of sound mind, Already seen

8 Who did Scott Baio play in the US sitcom *Happy Days*? Potsie, Richie, Chaci

9 Courtesy And Care is the motto of which organisation? Automobile Association, The Samaritans, National Health Service

10 In which country is King Khaled Airport located? Egypt, Kenya, Saudi Arabia

ANSWERS

1. Emerald 2. *The Golden Palace* 3. Loch Lomond 4. Hawaii 5. Fluffy
6. Head 7. Of sound mind 8. Chaci 9. Automobile Association
10. Saudi Arabia

QUIZ 89

• •

What words are represented by the following phrases
   from Cockney rhyming slang?

1   Biscuits and cheese   Knees, Fleas, Keys

2   Jam jar   Bar, Car, War

3   Cain and Abel   Fable, Stable, Table

4   Garden gate   Magistrate, Best mate, Fishing bait

5   Almond rocks   Docks, Locks, Socks

6   Syrup of fig   Oil rig, Jig, Wig

7   Band of hope   Rope, Soap, Pope

8   Weasel and stoat   Goat, Float, Coat

9   Bo Peep   Sleep, Deep, Creep

10   Butcher's hook   Look, Duck, Book

ANSWERS

1. Knees 2. Car 3. Table 4. Magistrate 5. Socks 6. Wig 7. Soap 8. Coat
9. Sleep 10. Look

QUIZ 90

• •

1 What is the oldest university in the USA?
   Princeton, Harvard, Columbia

2 Aardvarks are indigenous to which continent?
   South America, Africa, Asia

3 Mount Usbourne is the highest peak on which
   group of islands?   Canary Islands, Falkland Islands,
   Channel Islands

4 In which cathedral is the play *Murder In The
   Cathedral* set?   Canterbury, Hereford, Salisbury

5 In which country is the Cresta Run winter games
   venue located?   Switzerland, Canada, France

6 What is the state capital of Missouri?   Lansing,
   Baton Rouge, Jefferson City,

7 In which state of Australia is the city of Brisbane?
   New South Wales, Western Australia, Queensland

8 What is the surname of Buffy The Vampire Slayer?
   Summers, Autumns, Winters

9 In which castle was Princess Margaret born>
   Windsor, Leeds, Glamis

10 What is the last name of the bank manager in the
    US comedy series *The Beverly Hillbillies*?   Drysdale,
    Moses, Bodine

ANSWERS

1. Harvard 2. Africa 3. Falkland Islands 4. Canterbury 5. Switzerland
6. Jefferson City 7. Queensland 8. Summers 9. Glamis 10. Drysdale

QUIZ 91

1 What is the predominant colour on the flag of Australia?   Blue, Red, White

2 How many stars are depicted on the flag of China?   None, 5, 20

3 What plant is depicted on the flag of Mexico? Venus flytrap, Okra, Cactus

4 What is depicted on the flag of the Boy Scout Association?   Tent, Prince of Wales feathers, Wolf

5 What appears on the top left hand corner of the flag of Bermuda?   Lion, Union Jack, Crescent

6 How many red stripes are there on the flag of the USA?   7, 17, 20

7 How many different colours are there on the flag of Austria?   2, 3, 4

8 What creature is depicted on the flag of Egypt? Fish, Bird, Cat

9 What colour is the middle stripe on the flag of Belgium?   Yellow, Green, Red

10 How many rings are on the bottom row of the Olympic flag?   1, 2, 5

ANSWERS

1. Blue 2. 5 3. Cactus 4. Prince of Wales feathers 5. Union Jack 6. 7 7. 2
8. Bird 9. Yellow 10. 2

QUIZ 92

1 What is the world's largest island beginning with the letter B? Borneo, Bermuda, Baffin

2 What number is in the name of San Francisco's American football team? 29ers, 49ers, 99ers

3 Which series of books were illustrated by Ernest Shepherd? *Winnie The Pooh*, *The Narnia Chronicles*, *Harry Potter*

4 *The War Cry* is which organisation's newspaper? Salvation Army, Territorial Army, RAF

5 What word completes the title of the Alfred Hitchcock film, *Dial M For …*? *Madness*, *Murder*, *Mother*

6 An excess of which acid causes gout? Uric, Sulphuric, Lactic

7 Which US baseball team is known as The Padres? San Jose, Philadelphia, San Diego

8 What has been removed from a polled animal? Teeth, Wool, Horns

9 What was Rod Stewart's first number one single? Maggie May, Sailing, Baby Jane

10 Which airline was declared bankrupt in 1992? LOT, KLM, TWA

ANSWERS

1. Borneo 2. 49ers 3. *Winnie The Pooh* 4. Salvation Army 5. *Murder* 6. Uric
7. San Diego 8. Horns 9. Maggie May 10. TWA

QUIZ 93

• •

1 What is the most highly populated city in Brazil?
   Brasilia, Sao Paulo, Belo Horizonte

2 What religion are most people in Chile?
   Buddhist, Roman Catholic, Hindu

3 For which South American soccer club did Pele
   spend the majority of his playing career?
   Flamenco, Santos, River Plate

4 In which country is the city of Medellin?
   Argentina, Colombia, Peru

5 Which capital city of South America has the
   highest altitude?   La Paz, Lima, Bogota

6 Located in Ecuador, what is the name of the
   world's highest active volcano?   Bunkopaxi,
   Cribopaxi, Cotopaxi

7 Which city in Uruguay shares its name with a car
   manufacturer?   Mercedes, Porsche, Lotus

8 In which country did the lambada dance
   originate?   Argentina, Peru, Brazil

9 What is the official language of Bolivia?   Dutch,
   Spanish, Quecha

10 In Chile, what is the Ladeco?   National airline,
    Monetary unit, Monarch's palace

ANSWERS

1. Sao Paulo 2. Roman Catholic 3. Santos 4. Colombia 5. La Paz
6. Cotopaxi 7. Mercedes 8. Brazil 9. Spanish 10. National airline

QUIZ 94

1 In what month of the year does St Swithin's Day fall? September, July, January

2 Which football club play their home matches at Prenton Park? Torquay United, Tranmere Rovers, Bristol Rovers

3 Cut Throat Jake is the archenemy of which cartoon character? Popeye, Dangermouse, Captain Pugwash

4 In which film did Hayley Mills play twin sisters? *Dead Ringers*, *The Parent Trap*, *Sibling Rivalry*

5 What colour are the shirts worn by Irelands rugby union international team? White, Green, Red

6 What is the name of the Teletubbies' vacuum cleaner? Noo Noo, La La, To To

7 The fictional hero Zorro took his name from the Spanish for what? Wolf, Fox, Lion

8 Which Spanish city is served by San Pablo Airport? Malaga, Seville, Valencia

9 What is Michael Fish known for broadcasting on TV? Football results, Weather forecast, the news

10 In which US city is the headquarters of ABC Television? Detroit, Chicago, New York

ANSWERS

1.July 2.Tranmere Rovers 3.Captain Pugwash 4.*The Parent Trap* 5.Green
6.Noo Noo 7.Fox 8.Seville 9.The weather 10.New York

QUIZ 95

• •

1 What bird is in the title of a chart topping single by Fleetwood Mac?   Eagle, Flamingo, Albatross

2 What is the largest member of the penguin family?   Queen, Duke, Emperor

3 What was the first name of the character that earned John Wayne his only Oscar?   Rooster, Falcon, Hawk

4 What species of owl is Hedwig in the *Harry Potter* tales?   Snowy, Barn, Elf

5 What was the previous name of the Golden Hind, the flagship of Sir Francis Drake?   Pelican, Puffin, Peregrine

6 What bird has species called willow and long tailed?   Wren, Tit, Swift

7 Who made Worzel Gummidge?   The Chickenman, The Crowman, The Henman

8 Which group recorded Hotel California?   The Doves, The Eagles, The Byrds

9 Which sport was for many years officiated by Dickie Bird?   Tennis, Boxing, Cricket

10 What is the surname of the author that created Beau Geste?   Swift, Parrot, Wren

ANSWERS

1. Albatross 2. Emperor penguin 3. Rooster 4. Snowy owl 5. Pelican 6. Tit
7. The Crowman 8. The Eagles 9. Cricket 10. Wren

QUIZ 96

. . . .

1 Which film company employed the motto, Art For Arts Sake?   Disney, MGM, Universal

2 What is 20 percent of 40?   8, 10, 12

3 Which car manufacturer has made models called the Toledo and the Alhambra?   Seat, Toyota, Nissan

4 What is the third letter of the Greek alphabet? Delta, Gamma, Iota

5 How many points is the brown ball worth in snooker?   2, 3, 4

6 What is a bobolink?   Bird, Fish, Frog

7 What was the name of the detective agency in the US TV series *Moonlighting*?   Half Moon, Crescent Moon, Blue Moon

8 What colour is the background on the flag of the EU?   Gold, Blue, Green

9 In what decade did J Edgar Hoover take up the post of Director of the FBI?   1920s, 1940s, 1950s

10 What creatures lives in a vespiary?   Wasps, Ants, Termites

ANSWERS

1. MGM 2. 8 3. Seat 4. Gamma 5. 4 6. Bird 7. Blue Moon 8. Blue 9. 1920s 10. Wasps

QUIZ 97

1. In Greek mythology, who killed Achilles?   Rome, Troy, Paris

2. What is the name of the father of Zeus?   Jupiter, Cronos, Apollo

3. What type of creature raised Romulus and Remus?   Wolf, Tiger, Fox

4. Ceres is the Roman goddess of what?   The stars, Children, Agriculture

5. Who led the Argonauts?   Jason, Ulysses, Hercules

6. In Greek mythology who fell in love with his own reflection?   Narcissus, Adonis, Oedipus

7. Which mythical monster did Theseus seek out in the labyrinth?   Cyclops, Minotaur, Hydra

8. In Greek mythology what is the only creature that can kill a basilisk?   Minotaur, Weasel, Eagle

9. What is the only day of the week to be named after a goddess?   Tuesday, Thursday, Friday

10. In Arthurian legend who found the Holy Grail?   Sir Galahad, King Arthur, Merlin

ANSWERS

1. Paris 2. Cronos 3. Wolf 4. Agriculture 5. Jason 6. Narcissus 7. Minotaur
8. Weasel 9. Friday 10. Sir Galahad

QUIZ 98

1 Which role was played by Andrew Sachs in Fawlty Towers?   The Major, Manuel, Basil

2 Which pop star is the nephew of FA Cup finalist Roy Dwight?   Elton John, Mick Jagger, Ringo Starr

3 Who did Christopher Plummer portray in the film *Waterloo*?   Duke of Wellington, Napoleon Bonaparte, George III

4 What is the official national symbol of Wales? Dragon, Leek, Daffodil

5 What aid to road safety was invented by Percy Shaw?   Traffic lights, Cats eyes, Seat belts

6 How are the showbusiness duo of Ian and Janet Tough collectively known?   The Krankies, Dollar, The Chuckle Brothers

7 What fruit is a cross between a peach and a plum?   Passion fruit, Nectarine, Prune

8 How many kids were shrunk in the 1989 film *Honey I Shrunk The Kids*?   2, 4, 6

9 Which novel features a sailing vessel called the Pequod?   *Treasure Island*, *Billy Budd*, *Moby Dick*

10 Who sang I Am What I Am and I Will Survive? Aretha Franklin, Diana Ross, Gloria Gaynor

ANSWERS

1. Manuel 2. Elton John 3. Duke of Wellington 4. Daffodil 5. Cats eyes
6. The Krankies 7. Nectarine 8. 4 9. *Moby Dick* 10. Gloria Gaynor

QUIZ 99

1 How much do rooms cost to rent in 'King Of The Road'? 50 cents, 5 pounds, 10 dollars

2 Which song contains the line, "Jesus loves you more than you can say"? 'Pray', 'Mrs Robinson', 'God only knows'

3 Who is "strung out on lasers" in a David Bowie song? Major Tom, Aladdin Sane, Jean Genie

4 What time is the alarm clock set in 'Daydream Believer'? 1 o'clock, 3 o'clock, 6 o'clock

5 What occupation is mentioned in the first line of the Human League song, 'Don't You Want Me'? Waitress, Doctor, Painter

6 Which song opens with the line, "On a dark desert highway, cool wind in my hair"? 'Heartbreak Hotel', 'House Of Fun', 'Hotel California'

7 Who did Kenny Rogers beseech not to "take your love to town"? Lucille, Georgia, Ruby

8 What is the first part of the body mentioned in 'Bohemian Rhapsody'? Eyes, Spine, Heart

9 What colour is the sky in the song, 'California Dreaming'? Black, Grey, Blue

10 Which Beatles hit has the line, "If there's anything I can do"? 'From Me To You', 'She Loves You', 'Help"

ANSWERS

1. 50 cents 2. 'Mrs Robinson' 3. Jean Genie 4. 6 o'clock 5. Waitress
6. 'Hotel California' 7. Ruby 8. Eyes 9. Grey 10. 'From Me To You'

QUIZ 100

1 On which continent is the country of Mali?
   South America, Africa, North America

2 How many tentacles does a squid have? 6, 8, 10

3 Which singer's first chart topping single was
   entitled Can The Can? Kelly Marie, Olivia Newton
   John, Suzi Quatro

4 What first name has the character played by
   Helen Mirren in *Prime Suspect*? Julie, Joy, Jane

5 Which English football league club was managed
   by Jock Stein in 1978? Liverpool, Leeds, Everton

6 Which landmark is located on Bedloe's Island?
   Statue of Liberty, Taj Mahal, Eiffel Tower

7 What name is given to a score of 111 in cricket?
   Wellington, Napoleon, Nelson

8 Who played the leading lady of Yul Brynner in the
   film musical *The King And I*? Deborah Kerr, Doris
   Day, Debbie Reynolds

9 What city accompanies London in the Dickens
   novel *A Tale Of Two Cities*? Glasgow, Paris, Madrid

10 In what year was Michael Jackson born? 1956,
    1958, 1960

ANSWERS

1. Africa 2. 10 3. Suzi Quatro 4. Jane 5. Leeds 6. Statue of Liberty
7. Nelson 8. Deborah Kerr 9. Paris 10. 1958

QUIZ 101

• •

1 At which sporting venue is Swinley Bottom found?   Anfield, Aintree, Ascot

2 What A was invented by Jacques Cousteau in 1943?   Ashtray, Aqualung, Alarm clock

3 What is the capital of New York State?   Augusta, Albany, Austin

4 Which oil tanker ran aground off the coast of Brittany in 1978?   Avro, Amoco Cadiz, Allegiance

5 What is the name of the elder brother of Moses in the Bible?   Abraham, Amos, Aaron

6 What was the Roman name for England? Albion, Asia Minor, Avalon

7 Which state of the USA is mentioned in the lyrics of The Beatles song, 'Get Back'?   Arizona, Alabama, Alaska

8 What is the first name of the character played by Emma Chambers in *The Vicar Of Dibley*?   Adele, Angela, Alice

9 The axilla is the technical term for which part of the human body?   Ankle, Armpit, Arm

10 What is the most highly populated country in the world beginning with the letter A?   Australia, Argentina, Algeria

ANSWERS

1. Ascot 2. Aqualung 3. Albany 4. Amoco Cadiz 5. Aaron 6. Albion
7. Arizona 8. Alice 9. Armpit 10. Argentina

QUIZ 102

1 What does the H stand for in the computer abbreviation http?   Higher, Hyper, Hold

2 What disease was once known as the White Death?   Malaria, Tubercolosis, Typhoid

3 What was the last bit of the Cheshire Cat to vanish in Alice In Wonderland?   Tail, Grin, Paws

4 Who received the black spot from Blind Pew in Treasure Island?   Long John Silver, Billy Bones, Jim Hawkins

5 Which tower features in the Beatles song 'I Am A Walrus'?   CN Tower, Eiffel Tower, Blackpool Tower

6 How were Ellis, Acton and Currer Bell better known?   Bronte sisters, The Beverly Sisters, The Three Degrees

7 Which musical features the song, 'One Night In Bangkok'?   *Evita*, *Chess*, *Miss Saigon*

8 How many bottles of champagne comprise a magnum?   2, 6, 10

9 Who played the title role in the film western *High Plains Drifter*?   Clint Eastwood, John Wayne, Paul Newman

10 From which country does Camembert cheese originate?   Spain, Wales, France

ANSWERS

1. Hyper 2. Tubercolosis 3. Grin 4. Billy Bones 5. Eiffel Tower
6. Bronte sisters 7. *Chess* 8. 2 9. Clint Eastwood 10. France

QUIZ 103

1 Which European football club play their home games at the Stadium of Light? Bordeaux, Benfica, Bayern Munich

2 Which horse won the Grand National in 2002? Ben Nevis, Bindaree, Benny The Dip

3 What B is the name for water collected at the bottom of a boat? Brine, Ballast, Bilge

4 Which group won the Eurovision Song Contest in 1981? Bucks Fizz, Black Lace, Bardo

5 Nassau is the capital of where? Belize, Bulgaria, Bahamas

6 What does a cooper make for a living? Barrels, Beds, Bottles

7 Which city hosted the 1982 Commonwealth Games? Belfast, Brisbane, Bombay

8 What is a dish garnished with if served a la Bretonne? Berries, Beans, Broccoli

9 What is the name of the French stock exchange? Balourd, Breton, Bourse

10 Who were the beaten FA Cup finalists in 1983? Burnley, Blackburn, Brighton

ANSWERS

1. Benfica 2. Bindaree 3. Bilge 4. Bucks Fizz 5. Bahamas 6. Barrels
7. Brisbane 8. Beans 9. Bourse 10. Brighton

QUIZ 104

1 What is the capital of Tibet? Kathmandu, Lhasa, Singapore

2 Which Simon & Garfunkel song was a hit for the Bangles in 1988? 'Hazy Shade Of Winter', 'The Sound Of Silence', 'America'

3 Which peak overlooks the town of Fort William? Ben Nevis, Table Mountain, Mount Snowdon

4 What is bibliophobia the fear of? God, Babies, Books

5 In which European country did Tokay wine originate? Greece, Hungary, Bulgaria

6 What is the worlds largest bay? Botany Bay, Hudson Bay, The Bay of Bengal

7 Which pop group had a telephone conversation with Sylvia's Mother? Dr Hook, The Spin Doctors, Dr And The Medics

8 Which plant family does the asparagus belong to? Orchid, Iris, Lily

9 In which country is Europe's highest waterfall located? Russia, Norway, Portugal

10 What does the O stand for with regard to the area of South Africa, often abbreviated to OFS? Old, Outer, Orange

ANSWERS

1. Lhasa 2. 'Hazy Shade Of Winter' 3. Ben Nevis 4. Books 5. Hungary
6. Hudson Bay 7. Dr Hook 8 Lily 9. Norway 10. Orange (Orange Free State)

QUIZ 105

1 What name is given to an assembly of cardinals?
Cathedral, Conclave, Celeste

2 What is the alternative name for the bird also known as the landrail? Canary, Crow, Corncrake

3 Canberra and Nevada are both varieties of which vegetable? Carrot, Cauliflower, Cucumber

4 Which team won the FA Cup in 1987? Crystal Palace, Coventry City, Cardiff City

5 What does the C stand for in the song, 'A Christmas Alphabet'? Crackers, Candy, Carols

6 In the novel *Lady Chatterley's Lover*, what is Lady Chatterley's first name? Christine, Camilla, Constance

7 Which instrument is most associated with Julian Lloyd Webber? Castanets, Clarinet, Cello

8 Which flower has the scientific name of dianthus? Carnation, Chrysanthemum, Crocus

9 What is the 15th wedding anniversary? Coral, China, Crystal

10 What C is the name given to a segment of a garlic bulb? Cruet, Cleaver, Clove

ANSWERS

1. Conclave 2. Corncrake 3. Cauliflower 4. Coventry City 5. Candy
6. Constance 7. Cello 8. Carnation 9. Crystal 10. Clove

QUIZ 106

1 Which S pop group were Living Next Door To Alice?   Sweet, Smokie, Slade

2 Which British city is known as, The City of Dreaming Spires?   Lincoln, Bath, Oxford

3 James Earl Jones provided the voice for which *Star Wars* character?   Darth Vadar, Yoda, C-3PO

4 Which actor, who played James Bond, was born in Wales? David Niven, Roger Moore, Timothy Dalton

5 On a Monopoly board what completes a green set with Oxford Street and Bond Street?   Park Lane, Regent Street, Pentonville Road

6 In what year was Mount Everest first conquered? 1951, 1953, 1955

7 What is the nationality of the snooker star John Higgins?   Scottish, Canadian, South African

8 Which country is home to the wine growing area of the Barossa Valley?   Argentina, Australia, USA

9 What is canard on a French restaurant menu? Dumplings, Carrots, Duck

10 Which part of the body does the adjective pulmonic refer to? Legs, Larynx, Lungs

ANSWERS

1. Smokie 2. Oxford 3. Darth Vada 4. Timothy Dalton 5. Regent Street
6. 1953 7. Scottish 8. Australia 9. Duck 10. Lungs

QUIZ 107

1. What is the first name of Flash Gordon's girlfriend? Dale, Dorothy, Debra

2. What does a drosometer measure? Decibels, Dew, Distance

3. What did Allan Pinkerton found in 1850? Diners Club, Detective agency, Dairy

4. Ricky Ross provides lead vocals for which pop group? Deacon Blue, Dire Straits, D:Ream

5. What is the name of Derek Trotter's son in Only Fools And Horses? Denzel, Dave, Damian

6. What title is given to a chief minister of a cathedral? Dean, Diocese, Deacon

7. What was the maiden name of Nancy Reagan? Donaldson, Davis, Dixon

8. In which film did Michael Caine play a conman called Lawrence Jamieson? *Death Becomes Her*, *Dirty Rotten Scoundrels*, *Dressed To Kill*

9. What is the capital of Senegal? Dijon, Doha, Dakar

10. What is the middle name of Austin Powers? Danger, Dread, Debonair

ANSWERS

1. Dale 2. Dew 3. Detective agency 4. Deacon Blue 5. Damian 6. Dean
7. Davis 8. *Dirty Rotten Scoundrels* 9. Dakar 10. Danger

QUIZ 108

. . . .

1 In which century did King Canute rule England?
   7th, 9th, 11th

2 Ninian and Brent are both the names of what in
   the North Sea?   Oil fields, Islands, Sand banks

3 Which sport is analysed on the TV show The
   Morning Line? Fishing, Horse racing, Snooker

4 What type of food is quargel?   Bread, Cheese,
   Fruit

5 On which island did the film star Oliver Reed die?
   Crete, Malta, Sicily

6 What is the name of Frank and Betty Spencer's
   daughter in the comedy series *Some Mothers Do
   Ave' Em*?   Jessica, Anna, Tabitha

7 How many letters are in the Greek alphabet?   22,
   24, 26

8 In which country did kendo originate? Korea,
   Malaysia, Japan

9 What type of animal is Rowlf in The Muppet
   Show?   Frog, Bear, Dog

10 Zwei is the German word for what number? 2,
    10, 12

ANSWERS

1. 11th 2. Oil fields 3. Horse racing 4. Cheese 5. Malta 6. Jessica 7. 24
8. Japan 9. Dog 10. 2

QUIZ 109

1. Who is the Roman goddess of wisdom? Maia, Minerva, Marduk

2. What middle name was Muhammed Ali born with? Marvin, Marcellus, Michael

3. Which city hosted the 1976 Summer Olympics? Montreal, Mexico City, Moscow

4. What is the correct term for a bird's back? Maxilla, Midrib, Mantle

5. In the film *Finding Nemo*, what is the name of Nemo's father? Marlin, Malcolm, Mortimer

6. What does the M stand for with regard to the TV show M*A*S*H? Medical, Mobile, Military

7. Leofric, the husband of Lady Godiva, was Earl of where? Macedonia, Mercia, Montfort

8. What is the last name of Oscar in The Odd Couple? Maxwell, Madison. Millburn

9. According to superstition what is broken to give seven years bad luck? Mistletoe, Mirror, Mug

10. What was the first name of George Washington's wife? Melissa, Mary, Martha

ANSWERS

1. Minerva 2. Marcellus 3. Montreal 4. Mantle 5. Marlin 6. Mobile (Mobile Army Surgical Hospital) 7. Mercia 8. Madison 9. Mirror 10. Martha

QUIZ 110

1 Fremantle is the port of which Australian city?
   Canberra, Perth, Darwin

2 In the city of Venice, what is a vaporetta?   Bridge,
   Water bus, Ice cream vendor

3 How many cents are in a dime? 5, 10, 25

4 What plane was designed by Reginald Mitchell?
   Spitfire, Concorde, Boeing 747

5 What is the symbol for the star sign of Aquarius?
   Scales, Centaur, Water carrier

6 Who played Batman in the 1995 film *Batman
   Forever*?   Val Kilmer, Adam West, Michael Keaton

7 Which US comedy series featured the character of
   Sam Malone?   *Cheers*, *Friends*, *Seinfeld*

8 Where was the 2003 British Open golf
   championship held?   Royal Lytham, Royal St
   George, Royal Berkdale

9 What is the name of the male half of the
   Eurythmics?   Dave Berry, Dave Stewart, Dave
   Sylvian

10 Whose kidnap precipitated the Trojan War?
    Pegasus, Helen, Venus

ANSWERS

1. Perth 2. Water bus 3. 10 4. Spitfire 5. Water carrier 6. Val Kilmer
7. *Cheers* 8. Royal St George 9. Dave Stewart 10. Helen (formerly of Sparta,
then of Troy)

QUIZ 111

• •

1 Rio is the Spanish word for what?   Red, River, Road

2 What R is treated by the triple vaccine MMR?
   Rabies, Ringworm, Rubella

3 The spirit of King Arthur is said to visit the world
   in the form of which bird?   Raven, Robin, Rook

4 What musical term was coined by the American
   disc jockey Alan Freed?   Rock and Roll, Rap, Rave

5 Which of the following is a book of the Bible?
   Rebecca, Ruth, Ruby

6 Who painted The Night Watch?   Rodin, Renoir,
   Rembrandt

7 Who topped the UK singles charts with the song,
   'Deeply Dippy'?   Right Said Fred, Republica, Roxy
   Music

8 Of what is Iris the Greek goddess?   Rivers,
   Rainbows, Romance

9 What is the ninth month of the Muslim calendar?
   Ramadan, Rajab, Rabia

10 What does the second R stand for in the acronym
    RADAR?   Relay, Route, Ranging

ANSWERS

1. River 2. Rubella 3. Raven 4. Rock and Roll 5. Ruth 6. Rembrandt
7. Right Said Fred 8. Rainbows 9. Ramadan 10. Ranging

QUIZ 112

1 Who played the role of Azeem in the film *Robin Hood Prince Of Thieves*? Morgan Freeman, Jack Wild, Christian Slater

2 What colour is Bart Simpson's hair? Yellow, Blue, Purple

3 Which fellow actor did Farrah Fawcett marry in 1973? Dustin Hoffman, Lee Majors, Burt Reynolds

4 Who created Popeye? Walt Disney, Max Fleischer, Chuck Jones

5 Who founded Harpo Production Incorporated in 1986? Harpo Marx, Oprah Winfrey, Woody Allen

6 What did the rap star Puff Daddy change his name to in 2001? P Diddy, P Mummy, Puff Dragon

7 In what year did Brazil win their first soccer World Cup? 1954, 1958, 1962

8 In which country was the rock star Carlos Santana born? Mexico, Spain, Puerto Rica

9 What is the last name of the central family in *The Godfather* film trilogy? Soprano, Puzo, Corleone

10 What name is given to a number one wood in the game of golf? Putter, Wedge, Driver

ANSWERS

1. Morgan Freeman 2. Yellow 3. Lee Majors 4. Max Fleischer 5. Oprah Winfrey 6. P Diddy 7. 1958 8. Mexico 9. Corleone 10. Driver

QUIZ 113

. . . .

1 What does a conchologist collect?   Shells, Stamps, Shoes

2 Which club won the FA Cup in 1976? Southampton, Sunderland, Stoke City

3 What is the capital of Costa Rica?   San Domingo, San Jose, San Sebastian

4 Which film starring Meryl Streep was adapted from a novel by William Styron?   *Silkwood*, *Sophie's Choice*, *Still Of The Night*

5 In cricket, what name are given to extras in Australia?   Spares, Sundries, Surpluses

6 Who performed the Dance Of The Seven Veils in the Bible?   Salmanazar, Salome, Sarah

7 What does the S stand for in the name of the author CS Forester?   Spencer, Scott, Simon

8 In which country is the Nubian Desert?   Spain, Syria, Sudan

9 What was the highest grossing box office film of the 1970s? *Star Wars*, *Saturday Night Fever*, *Superman*

10 Which city hosted the 1988 Summer Olympics? Seoul, Stockholm, Sydney

ANSWERS

1. Shells 2. Southampton 3. San Jose 4. *Sophie's Choice* 5. Sundries
6. Salome 7. Scott 8. Sudan 9. *Star Wars* 10. Seoul

QUIZ 114

1 Which country has the longest coastline in Europe? France, Norway, Sweden

2 In which century did the author Jules Verne die? 19th, 20th, 21st

3 What colour are the shorts worn by Mickey Mouse? Black, Red, Blue

4 What is the name of Captain Hook's first mate in Peter Pan? Smog, Smee, Smurt

5 Who was the adopted son of Emperor Claudius? Caligula, Nero, Tiberius

6 What nationality was the 16th century astrologer Nostradamus? Greek, Italian, French

7 How many dots are on a pair of dice? 36, 42, 44

8 Which country is known as, The Switzerland of Africa? Ghana, Swaziland, Tunisia

9 Who was the first king to be crowned at Westminster Abbey? William the Conqueror, Edward the Confessor, Charles I

10 Which football club are nicknamed The Addicks? Portsmouth, Charlton Athletic, Rochdale

ANSWERS

1. Norway 2. 20th 3. Red 4. Smee 5. Nero 6. French 7. 42 8. Swaziland
9. William the Conqueror 10. Charlton Athletic

QUIZ 115

• •

1 On which river does Rome stand? Tagus, Tiber, Tigris

2 What is the capital of Albania? Tunis, Tehran, Tirana

3 What does the T stand for in the Disney park acronym, EPCOT? Tomorrow, Time, Terrestrial, Technology

4 Where was the biblical St Paul born? Tel Aviv, Tunisia, Tarsus

5 What is the nickname of Bolton Wanderers FC? Trotters, Terriers, Tigers

6 Golden Queen is a variety of which herb? Tarragon, Thyme, Thrift

7 What does a grabatologist collect? Ties, Toys, Train numbers

8 What animal precedes the rabbit in the Chinese calendar? Turkey, Tiger, Tortoise

9 What acknowledgement is given in fencing when a hit is scored? Trappe, Touche, Tallyho

10 What is the hobby of a gricer? Train spotting, Table tennis, Tiddlywinks

ANSWERS

1. Tiber 2. Tirana 3. Tomorrow (Experimental Prototype Community of Tomorrow) 4. Tarsus 5. Trotters 6. Thyme 7. Ties 8. Tiger 9. Touche 10. Train spotting

QUIZ 116

....

1. In which English county does *Harry Potter* live with the Dursleys? Surrey, Essex, Suffolk

2. What is known as, The Ship of the Desert? Jeep, Camel, Horse

3. Which French football star scored the goal in the 1996 FA Cup final? Cantona, Anelka, Henry

4. What was Lech Walesa's occupation when he founded the Solidarity Trade Union? Miner, Electrician, Builder

5. What was a blunderbuss? Train, Dress, Gun

6. What is the nickname of Coventry City FC? Sky Blues, Red Devils, Green Giants

7. Which film earned Kevin Spacey his first Best Actor Oscar? *Seven*, *American Beauty*, *The Negotiator*

8. Who wrote the book, *Taken On Trust*, after being released from captivity? Nelson Mandela, Terry Waite, Mike Tyson

9. Which TV series featured teachers called Miss Sherwood and Miss Grant? *Fame*, *Head Of The Class*, *Grange Hill*

10. How many games did Arsenal FC lose in the 2003/04 Premiership season? None, 5, 10

ANSWERS

1. Surrey 2. Camel 3. Eric Cantona 4. Electrician 5. Gun 6. Sky Blues
7. *American Beauty* 8. Terry Waite 9. *Fame* 10. None

QUIZ 117

1 What F is the collective noun for a group of piglets?   Foundling, Farrow, Feast

2 What L was the name of the first space probe that landed on the moon in 1959?   Luna 2, Lexus 2, Leader 2

3 Which R won the Grand National in 1995?   Red Rum, Royal Athlete, Rhyme N Reason

4 Which US state, beginning with I, is one of the eight Rocky Mountain states?   Iowa, Idaho, Illinois

5 What J is the middle name of *Harry Potter*?   John, James, Jack

6 What P is detected by a Gravindex test?   Pollen, Polio, Pregnancy

7 What L was the name of the space craft in the sci-fi TV series *Blake's Seven*? Liberator, Landscape, Leviathan

8 What P is the 30th wedding anniversary? Pearl, Platinum, Pottery

9 What N is the name given to a young grasshopper?   Newt, Neft, Nymph

10 What N is the collective noun for a group of pheasants?   Nest, Nye, Nap

ANSWERS

1. Farrow 2. Luna 2 3. Royal Athlete 4. Idaho 5. James 6. Pregnancy
7. Liberator 8. Pearl 9. Nymph 10. Nye

QUIZ 118

1 What can be vulgar, proper, improper, common and simple?   Fractions, Nouns, Triangles

2 What is the world's most poisonous fish?   Stonefish, Shalefish, Pebblefish

3 Which Arthurian character shares his name with a variety of falcon?   Galahad, Merlin, Lancelot

4 Which former First Lady of the USA penned the autobiography, Living History?   Hillary Clinton, Jackie Kennedy, Patricia Nixon

5 How many soccer World Cups did Brazil win in the 20th century?   3, 4, 6

6 What was sold to the British Museum for £36,000 in 1816?   Crown Jewels, Elgin Marbles, Dead Sea Scrolls

7 Which musical instrument is described as magic in the title of an opera?   Harp, Piano, Flute

8 How many teeth are in a full human adult set?   28, 32, 38

9 What is the only animal that has four knees?   Rhinoceros, Elephant, Hippopotamus

10 Which TV series features a vehicle called The Mystery Machine?   *The X Files*, *Scooby Doo*, *Murder She Wrote*

ANSWERS

1. Fractions 2. Stonefish 3. Merlin 4. Hillary Clinton 5. 4 6. Elgin Marbles
7. Flute 8. 32 9. Elephant 10. *Scooby Doo*

QUIZ 119

• •

1 Which of the following does not appear in the novel *Oliver Twist*? Sarah Gamp, Fagin, Jack Dawkins

2 Which European countries does the Alps not extend into? France, Spain, Switzerland

3 Who did not accompany Dorothy Gale to meet the Wizard of Oz? Hickory, Scar, HZeke

4 Which of the following is not a murder weapon in the board game of Cluedo? Candlestick, Dagger, Rifle

5 Which of the following US states does not border Mexico? Texas, Colorado, Arizona

6 Which of the following is not one of the seven virtues? Faith, Patience, Fortitude

7 Which of these is not a prime number? 17, 27, 37

8 Which of the following races is not part of the Triple Crown in British horse racing? The Oaks, 2000 Guineas, The Derby

9 Which President's head is not depicted on Mount Rushmore? Nixon, Lincoln, Washington

10 Which of the following is not the name of a Teenage Mutant Ninja Turtle? Leonardo, Michelangelo, Rembrandt

ANSWERS

1. *Sarah Gamp* 2. Spain 3. Scar 4. Rifle 5. Colorado 6. Patience 7. 27
8. 2000 Guineas 9. Nixon 10. Rembrandt

QUIZ 120

1 What is the name of the home village of Miss Marple? St Mary Mead, St Joan Mead, St Catherine Mead

2 In what language was the Magna Carta written? English, Latin, Gaelic

3 Which island was invaded by the Allies in Operation Husky in 1943? Cyprus, Malta, Sicily

4 What is the world's longest mountain range? Rockies, Himalayas, Andes

5 What are the front teeth between the canines called? Molars, Incisors, Pre-molars

6 Which country surrendered in World War II aboard USS Missouri? Germany, Italy, Japan

7 Which train serves the island of Sodor? Flying Scotsman, Orient Express, Thomas the Tank Engine

8 What is the UK's oldest Sunday newspaper? *The Observer*, *The News Of The World*, *The People*

9 In which TV series did Commander Shore declare, "Stand by for action, anything can happen in the next half hour"? *Thunderbirds*, *Stingray*, **Joe 90**

10 Which detective made his debut in the novel *The Big Sleep*? Sam Spade, Dick Tracy, Philip Marlowe

ANSWERS

1. St Mary Mead 2. Latin 3. Sicily 4. Andes 5.Incisors 6. Japan 7. *Thomas the Tank Engine* 8. *The Observer* 9. *Stingray* 10.Philip Marlowe

QUIZ 121

1 Which sporting trophy was originally called, The Inter Cities Fairs Cup?   World Series, UEFA Cup, FA Cup

2 In which city did Anne Frank write her famed diary?   Paris, Amsterdam, Warsaw

3 What is the modern day name of Constantinople? Baghdad, Istanbul, Amman

4 Which capital city lies on the island of Luzon? Copenhagen, Manila, Wellington

5 What was the capital of India at the start of the 20th century?   Calcutta, Bombay, Agra

6 In which city did an earthquake result in over 7,000 deaths in 1985?   Lima, Tokyo, Mexico City

7 In which city was the prophet Mohammed born? Ulan Bator, Mecca, Jerusalem

8 In which city did Rudolph Hess die whilst incarcerated in Spandau Prison?   Berlin, Graz, Bonn

9 What is the capital of Trinidad and Tobago?   Port Of Paraguay, Port Of Brazil, Port Of Spain

10 What was the capital of England prior to London? Winchester, Manchester, Colchester

ANSWERS

1. UEFA Cup 2. Amsterdam 3. Istanbul 4. Manila 5. Calcutta 6. Mexico City
7. Meccar 8. Berlin 9. Port Of Spain 10. Winchester

QUIZ 122

1 What is the middle name of former US President Jimmy Carter?   Duke, Earl, Lord

2 In order to copyright his face, a clown paints his image onto a what?   Football, Egg, Plate

3 What name is given to the boundary of a circle? Contour, Radius, Circumference

4 What sport takes place at the Racecourse Ground in Derby?   Horse racing, Football, Cricket

5 What is calamari on a restaurant menu?   Wine, Squid, Prawns

6 Which Dickens novel is sub-titled the *Parish Boys Progress*?   *David Copperfield*, *Oliver Twist*, *Barnaby Rudge*

7 A Flemish Giant is a breed of what?   Pig, Rabbit, Goat

8 Sam Ryan features in which TV crime drama? *Prime Suspect*, *The Gentle Touch*, *Silent Witness*

9 Who scored the opening goal for Manchester United in the 1999 FA Cup final?   David Beckham, Teddy Sheringham, Roy Keane

10 Which of the Monty Python team penned the 1996 novel *Hemingway's Chair*?   John Cleese, Michael Palin, Graham Chapman

ANSWERS

1 Earl 2. Egg 3. Circumference 4. Cricket 5. Squid 6. *Oliver Twist* 7. Rabbit
8. *Silent Witness* 9. Teddy Sheringham 10. Michael Palin

QUIZ 123

1 By what name is ascorbic acid otherwise known?
   Vinegar, Vitamin C, Olive Oil

2 Which planet provides the alternative title of a
   Mozart symphony?   Earth, Jupiter, Venus

3 What is the more common name for magnesium
   silicate?   Talcum powder, Pepper, Rust

4 By what name is Laurence Tureaud better known?
   Lawrence Of Arabia, Stan Laurel, Mr T

5 By what name is the ant bear also known?
   Aardvark, Sloth, Armadillo

6 What is the stage name of the comedian born
   Robert Harper?   Bobby Davro, Bobby Ball, Bob
   Monkhouse

7 By what colourful name was Paul Neal better
   known?   Al Green, Barry White, Red Adair

8 What is the alternative name of The Collegiate
   Church of St Peter?   York Minster, Westminster
   Abbey, Canterbury Cathedral

9 Which African country is Mount Kilimanjaro in?
   Tanzania, Sudan, South Africa

10 Which singer was born Michelle Wallen?   Mica
   Paris, Melanie, Melissa Manchester

ANSWERS

1. Vitamin C 2. Jupiter 3. Talcum powder 4. Mr T 5. Aardvark 6. Bobby Ball
7. Red Adair 8. Westminster Abbey 9. Tanzania 10. Mica Paris

QUIZ 124

1 Which medal bears the inscription, For Gallantry?
George Cross, USA Congressional Medal Of Honor,
Purple Heart

2 On which island was Captain James Cook killed?
Cuba, Hawaii, Tasmania

3 What was the nationality of the winner of the
2003 Tour de France? French, Belgian, American

4 What has species called 2 spot, 7 spot and 14
spot? Ladybird, Tarantula, Leopard

5 What gas is produced by the Haber Bosch
process? Neon, Helium, Ammonia

6 What shape is an object described as
campanulate? Star, Horseshoe, Bell

7 How many states of the USA have a name
beginning and ending with the letter A? 2, 3, 4

8 What was the nationality of the legendary lover
Casanova? French, Welsh, Italian

9 How many gold medals did Carl Lewis win at the
1984 Summer Olympics? 2, 4, 6

10 King Olaf, who died in 1991, was the monarch of
which European country? Sweden, Norway,
Denmark

ANSWERS

1. George Cross 2. Hawaii 3. American (Lance Armstrong) 4. Ladybird
5. Ammonia 6. Bell 7. 3 8. Italian 9. 4 10. Norway

QUIZ 125

Identify the solo artists from three of their hit singles

1 'Daughter of Darkness', 'Help Yourself', 'Kiss' Frank Sinatra, Prince, Tom Jones

2 'The Man With The Child In His Eyes', 'Wow', 'Running Up That Hill' Boy George, Kate Bush, David Bowie

3 'Sometimes', 'Lucky', 'You Drive Me Crazy' Christina Aguilera, Britney Spears, Holly Valance

4 'Hot Dog', 'Oh Julie', 'Merry Christmas Everyone' Alvin Stardust, Shakin' Stevens, Slade

5 'The Boat That I Row', 'Shout', 'I'm A Tiger' Lulu, Cilla Black, Sandie Shaw

6 'Strong Enough', 'One And One', 'Believe' Madonna, Dido, Cher

7 'Leave Right Now', 'Light My Fire', 'Evergreen' Gareth Gates, Will Young, Michelle McManus

8 'Tell Her About It', 'The Longest Time', 'Just The Way You Are' Barry White, Billy Joel, Van Morrison

9 'Please Don't Tease', 'The Minute Your Gone', 'The Twelfth Of Never' Donny Osmond, Cliff Richard, Billy Fury

10 'Two Hearts', 'You Can't Hurry Love', 'Sussudio' The Supremes, Phil Collins, Jason Donavan

ANSWERS

1. Tom Jones 2. Kate Bush 3. Britney Spears 4. Shakin' Stevens 5. Lulu
6. Cher 7. Will Young 8. Billy Joel 9. Cliff Richard 10. Phil Collins

QUIZ 126

1 Lake Garda is the largest lake in which country?
   Germany, Italy, Northern Ireland

2 The marmoset is the smallest member of which
   animal family?   Rodent, Squirrel, Monkey

3 Who created the characters of Flopsy, Mopsy and
   Cottontail?   Dodie Smith, Mary Norton, Beatrix Potter

4 Mike D'Abo provided lead vocals for which group?
   The Kinks, The Seekers, Manfred Mann

5 Which infamous prison was closed in 1963?
   Spandau, Alcatraz, Broadmoor

6 Which literary character fell asleep in the Catskill
   mountains?   Rip Van Winkle, Snow White, Heidi

7 In what decade was the National Health Service
   founded in Britain?   1920s, 1930s, 1940s

8 In which sport is a Malibu board used?   Squash,
   Gymnastics, Surfing

9 Which pop duo had the surnames of Moore and
   Prater?   Sam and Dave, Peter and Gordon, Jan and
   Dean

10 In which TV series did Father O'Connell replace Father
   Clifford?   *The Thorn Birds*, *Father Ted*, *Ballykissangel*

ANSWERS

1. Italy 2. Monkey 3. Beatrix Potter 4. Manfred Mann 5. Alcatraz 6. Rip Van
Winkle 7. 1940s 8. Surfing 9. Sam and Dave 10. *Ballykissangel*

QUIZ 127

• •

Which film star links each group of three films?

1 *The Alamo, Madigan, Who Dares Wins* Richard
   Widmark, John Wayne, Gary Cooper

2 *The Great Escape, Sister Act II, The Baltimore Bullet*
   Charles Bronson, David McCallum, James Coburn

3 *Ghost, The Outsiders, Red Dawn*   Demi Moore,
   Charlie Sheen, Patrick Swayze

4 *Jurassic Park, The Tall Guy, Independence Day*   Will
   Smith, Sam Neill, Jeff Goldblum

5 *A Star Is Born, Heaven's Gate, Alice Doesn't Live Here
   Anymore* Kris Kristofferson, Judy Garland, James
   Mason

6 *The Towering Inferno, The Music Lovers, The Three
   Musketeers* Paul Newman, Oliver Reed, Richard
   Chamberlain

7 *Romancing The Stone, Jack The Bear, Ruthless People*
   Joe Pesci, Kathleen Turner, Danny DeVito

8 *Ocean's Eleven, The Mexican, Thelma & Louise* Julia
   Roberts, Brad Pitt, Susan Sarandon

9 *Easy Rider, Speed, Blue Velvet*   Keanu Reeves,
   Dennis Hopper, Peter Fonda

10 *Edward Scissorhands, Little Women, Heathers*
   Johnny Depp, Sigourney Weaver, Winona Ryder

ANSWERS

1. Richard Widmark 2. James Coburn 3. Patrick Swayze 4. Jeff Goldblum
5. Kris Kristofferson 6. Richard Chamberlain 7. Danny DeVito 8. Brad Pitt
9. Dennis Hopper 10. Winona Ryder

QUIZ 128

1 Who joined Coronation Street in 2004 as Ernie Crabbe? Jimmy Nail, Norman Wisdom, Jim Dale

2 What crop is attacked by the Colorado beetle? Wheat, Rice, Potato

3 What is the playing area of a baseball pitch called? Square, Diamond, Circle

4 Which of the following biblical characters is renowned for his wisdom? Job, Solomon, Jonah

5 In which type of auction is the price of an item reduced until a buyer is found? Spanish auction, Greek auction, Dutch auction

6 Which British stately home is known as the Palace of the Peak? Buckingham Palace, Castle Howard, Chatsworth House

7 What is the only sea in the world that has no coastline? Sargasso, Tasman, Red

8 Which country does the football star Zinedine Zidane represent? Brazil, France, Germany

9 Which film sequel is advertised with the tag line, "Same planet, new scum"? *Men In Black II*, *Aliens*, *Terminator II*

10 What part of the body does a dermatologist care for? Skin, Muscles, Feet

ANSWERS

1. Norman Wisdom 2. Potato 3. Diamond 4. Solomon 5. Dutch auction
6. Chatsworth House 7. Sargasso Sea 8. France 9. *Men In Black II* 10. Skin

QUIZ 129

• •

In which TV show did …

1 Paul Shane play Ted Bovis? *You Rang My Lord, Hi-De -Hi, Holby City*

2 Angela Baddeley play Kate Bridges? *Upstairs Downstairs, The Forsyte Saga, Tenko*

3 Penelope Keith play Margo Leadbetter? *To The Manor Born, The Good Life, Executive Stress*

4 Maurice Gosfield play Private Duane Doberman? *M*A*S*H, Dad's Army, Sergeant Bilko*

5 Leonard Nimoy play Paris? *Mission Impossible, The Man From UNCLE, Star Trek: The Next Generation*

6 David Dixon play Ford Prefect? *Red Dwarf, Hitchhikers Guide To The Galaxy, Blake's Seven*

7 Frances De La Tour play Ruth Jones? *Mrs Thursday, Alias Smith And Jones, Rising Damp*

8 Edward Woodward play Robert McCall? *Callan, The Equaliser, The Professionals*

9 Cheryl Ladd play Kris Munroe? *Baywatch, Cagney And Lacey, Charlie's Angels*

10 Brian Blessed play King Richard IV? *Blackadder, Robin of Sherwood, I Claudius*

ANSWERS

1. *Hi-De -Hi* 2. *Upstairs Downstairs* 3. *The Good Life* 4. *Sergeant Bilko*
5. *Mission Impossible* 6. *Hitchhikers Guide To The Galaxy* 7. *Rising Damp*
8. *The Equaliser* 9. *Charlie's Angels* 10. *Blackadder*

QUIZ 130

. . . .

1 What does the A stand for in the acronym AWOL?
   Army, Absent, Action

2 In which country did duffel coats originate?
   Belgium, Bulgaria, Romania

3 Which alcoholic drink is nicknamed Nelson's
   Blood?   Brandy, Rum, Red wine

4 What colour provides the surname of Rachel in
   Friends?   Brown, Black, Green

5 How many humans took refuge aboard Noah's
   Ark?   2, 8, 12

6 Which 1988 film told the story of the Profumo
   Affair?   *Buster*, *Scandal*, *The Long Good Friday*

7 What provides the staple diet of badgers?   Grass,
   Worms, Birds eggs

8 What is the smallest county in Northern Ireland?
   Antrim, Fermanagh, Armagh

9 What is the home state of the literary sleuth
   Jessica Fletcher?   Maryland, Mississippi, Maine

10 Which city is home to Sing Sing Prison?   Tokyo,
   New York, Bangkok

ANSWERS

1. Absent (Absent without leave) 2. Belgium 3. Rum 4. Green 5. 8
6. *Scandal* 7. Worms 8. Armagh 9. Maine 10. New York

QUIZ 131

Who created each pair of literary characters

1 Charlie Bucket and Willy Wonka   Elizabeth
   Beresford, Roald Dahl, Raymond Briggs

2 The Invisible Man and the Morlocks   William
   Golding, John Steinbeck, HG Wells

3 Jeremy Fisher and Johnny Townmouse   James
   Herriott, Beatrix Potter, AA Milne

4 Noddy and Frederick Trottevillen   Enid Blyton,
   Hans Christian Andersen, Anita Loos

5 Professor Binns and Hermione Granger   Jan Mark,
   JK Rowling, Nick Hornby

6 John Jarndyce and Augustus Snodgrass   John
   Fowles, Mark Twain, Charles Dickens

7 Jonathan Harker and Professor Van Helsing   Mary
   Shelley, Jack London, Bram Stoker

8 Samwise Gamgee and Saruman the White   CS
   Lewis, Lewis Carroll, J R R Tolkien

9 Ernst Blofeld and Caractacus Potts   Raymond
   Chandler, Ian Fleming, Leslie Charteris

10 Catherine Earnshaw and Heathcliffe   Emily Bronte,
    Harper Lee, Charlotte Bronte

ANSWERS

1. Roald Dahl 2. HG Wells 3. Beatrix Potter 4. Enid Blyton 5. JK Rowling
6. Charles Dickens 7. Bram Stoker 8. J R R Tolkien 9. Ian Fleming
10. Emily Bronte

QUIZ 132

1 In which country was William Tell born?   Austria, Germany, Switzerland

2 In which country was the TV comedy special, *One Foot In The Algarve* set?   Portugal, Spain, France

3 Let Not The Deep Swallow Me Up, is the motto of which organisation?   P & O Ferries, Royal National Lifeboat Institution, Cunard Line

4 What colour are pistachio nuts?   Black, Red, Green

5 Photophobia is the morbid fear of what?   Light, Televisions, Cameras

6 Which biblical character said, "I find no fault with this man"?   Jesus Christ, Pontius Pilate, John the Baptist

7 On a Spanish restaurant menu, what are gambas? Potatoes, Prawns, Onions

8 What was the name of the 1980s backing group of the singer Kid Creole?   Cranberries, Rocking Berries, Coconuts

9 What model of Ford car did Starsky & Hutch drive? Torino, Zephyr, Capri

10 Which film earned Lee Marvin his only Oscar?   *Paint Your Wagon*, *Cat Ballou*, *The Dirty Dozen*

ANSWERS

1. Switzerland 2. Portugal 3. Royal National Lifeboat Institution 4. Green
5. Light 6. Pontius Pilate 7. Prawns 8. Coconuts 9. Torino 10. *Cat Ballou*

QUIZ 133

1 Which member of The Simpsons family plays the saxophone? Bart, Lisa, Marge

2 What is Paddington Bear's favourite food? Honey, Marmalade sandwiches, Doughnuts

3 Which children's character lives in House For One? Rupert Bear, Big Ears, Noddy

4 What animal is the foe of Little Red Riding Hood? Bear, Fox, Wolf

5 What is the name of Barney Rubble's baby son in The Flintstones? Bam Bam, Bang Bang, Biff Biff

6 What type of animal is Sawtooth in the cartoon series *Wacky Races*? Dragon, Beaver, Rat

7 Who lived in a land called Honalee? Puff the Magic Dragon, The Teletubbies, Ivor the Engine

8 Which children's favourites accompanied Father Abraham? The Clangers, The Smurfs, The Tweenies

9 In the original fairytale of Cinderella, what were Cinderella's slippers made from? Fur, Gold, Rubies

10 Who was the first animated character to be honoured with a star on Hollywood's Walk of Fame? Mickey Mouse, Bugs Bunny, Betty Boop

ANSWERS

1. Lisa 2. Marmalade sandwiches 3. Noddy 4. Wolf, Bear, Fox, Rat
5. Bam Bam 6. Beaver 7. Puff the Magic Dragon 8. The Smurfs 9. Fur
10. Mickey Mouse

QUIZ 134

1 Which planet is known as the Horned Planet?
Earth, Venus, Mars

2 What is produced by the lachrymal glands?
Saliva, Tears, Sweat

3 What animal family does the chipmunk belong
to? Rat, Bear, Squirrel

4 What is known as the Lungs of New York? Times
Square, Wall Street, Central Park

5 Which Asian country first hosted a Formula One
Grand Prix? Korea, Japan, China

6 In which film did Tom Cruise play Cole Trickle?
The Firm, *Days Of Thunder*, *Mission Impossible*

7 How was William Bonney better known? Billy The
Kid, Buffalo Bill, Wild Bill Hickok

8 Who was the first England cricket star to play in
100 Test matches? Ian Botham, David Gower,
Colin Cowdrey

9 In the TV soap *EastEnders*, how did Nick Cotton's
son Ashley die? Shot, Motorcycle accident,
Poisoned

10 What is the collective noun for a group of
widows? Knit, Mourning, Ambush

ANSWERS

1. Venus 2. Tears 3. Squirrel 4. Central Park 5. Japan 6. *Days Of Thunder*
7. Billy The Kid 8. Colin Cowdrey 9. Motorcycle accident 10. Ambush

QUIZ 135

. . . .

1 What sport is played by the Boston Celtics?
   Baseball, Basketball, Hockey

2 Peter Ebdon and Ken Doherty have both been
   crowned world champion in which sport?
   Badminton, Snooker, Speedway

3 Which sport awards penalties for slashing, holing
   and spearing? Fencing, Kendo, Ice hockey

4 What name is given to the Scottish version of
   hockey? Curling, Lacrosse, Shinty

5 In which sport do competitors negotiate eddies
   and stoppers? Downhill skiing, Canoeing, Surfing

6 In which sport are the cradle grip and the claw
   grip employed? Tug of war, Bowls, Golf

7 In which sport do contestants take a practice shot
   known as a bluffie? Archery, Biathlon, Croquet

8 At which sport did Prince William captain the Eton
   school team? Polo, Rugby league, Swimming

9 John Curry won an Olympic gold medal for Britain
   in which event? Pentathlon, Rowing, Ice skating

10 What sport is played at Happy Valley in Hong
   Kong? Cycling, Horse racing, Kung Fu

ANSWERS

1. Basketball 2. Snooker 3. Ice hockey 4. Shinty 5. Canoeing 6. Bowls
7. Archery 8. Swimming 9. Ice skating 10. Horse racing

QUIZ 136

• •

1 What is the smallest state of the USA?   Hawaii, Rhode Island, New Jersey

2 Jaffa oranges were named after a port in which country?   Portugal, Israel, Saudi Arabia

3 What is the official language of Fiji?   French, English, Dutch

4 What is the name of Scooby Doo's nephew? Scooby Don't, Scooby Did, Scrappy Doo

5 Who plays Queen Amadala in the *Star Wars* films? Carrie Fisher, Lucy Liu, Natalie Portman

6 Who entered the House of Lords in 1992 as Baroness of Kesteven?   Betty Boothroyd, Shirley Williams, Margaret Thatcher

7 Whose secretary was called Della Street?   Jim Bergerac, Sherlock Holmes, Perry Mason

8 What name is given to a moon between a half moon and a full moon?   Gibbous moon, New moon, Crescent moon

9 Who won her first Wimbledon Singles title in 1974?   Billie Jean King, Chris Evert, Sue Barker

10 Purple Emperor and Painted Lady are both varieties of what?   Butterfly, Bird, Plum

ANSWERS

1. Rhode Island 2. Israel 3. English 4. Scrappy Doo 5. Natalie Portman
6. Margaret Thatcher 7. Perry Mason 8. Gibbous moon 9. Chris Evert
10. Butterfly

QUIZ 137

• •

What name is given to the female of the species of
   the following animals?

1 Cat   Princess, Queen, Duchess

2 Donkey   Mary, Winnie, Jenny

3 Ferret   Jill, Molly, Foal

4 Bear   Filly, Sow, Buck

5 Rabbit   Dray, Doe, Doll

6 Salmon   Fry, Hen, Pen

7 Fox   Vixen, Cat, Bitch

8 Goat   Granny, Grace, Nanny

9 Moose   Mare, Cow, Shoat

10 Peacock   Peachick, Peasquab, Peahen

ANSWERS

1. Queen 2. Jenny 3. Jill 4. Sow 5. Doe 6. Hen 7. Vixen 8. Nanny 9. Cow
10. Peahen

QUIZ 138

. . . .

1 What year witnessed the assassination of Indira Gandhi? 1974, 1984, 1994

2 What is Tom Sawyer's hometown? Jamestown, Georgetown, St Petersburg

3 What are the three pipes on a set of bagpipes called? Stops, Drones, Bellows

4 What is Snoopy's feathered friend called in the Peanuts cartoon? Ringo, Linus, Woodstock

5 Which native American chief was also known by the name of Tatanka Iyotanka? Sitting Bull, Geronimo, Crazy Horse

6 What title is given to the head of state in Kuwait? Aga, Sultan, Emir

7 In 1963, who became the first actress to be paid a fee of $1 million for one film? Sophia Loren, Elizabeth Taylor, Audrey Hepburn

8 Who wrote The Ballad Of Reading Gaol? George Bernard Shaw, Oscar Wilde, DH Lawrence

9 What was Connie Booth's character's name in *Fawlty Towers*? Holly, Polly, Molly

10 In which 1974 film did Jack Nicholson play the character of Jake Gittes? *One Flew Over The Cuckoo's Nest, The Shining, Chinatown*

ANSWERS

1. 1984 2. St Petersburg 3. Drones 4. Woodstock 5. Sitting Bull 6. Emir
7. Elizabeth Taylor 8. Oscar Wilde 9. Polly 10. *Chinatown*

QUIZ 139

• •

1 Who had a hit with 'Crazy in Love' in 2003?
   Victoria Beckham, Beyonce Knowles, Mel C

2 Which band had a 60's hit with 'Go Now'?   Pink
   Floyd, The Moody Blues, Black Lace

3 Which Irish band topped the UK charts with the
   song 'Breathless' in 2000?   U2, Westlife, The Corrs

4 Which song was a 1991 hit for Michael Jackson?
   'Dirty Diana', 'Black Or White', 'Smooth Criminal'

5 What toys did the two little boys own in the Rolf
   Harris hit?   Tin soldier, Teddy bear, Wooden horse

6 Which song was a hit for Norman Greenbaum?
   'Spirit In The Sky', 'Suspicious Minds', 'American Pie'

7 Who collaborated with Elton John on the 1991
   chart topper 'Don't Let The Sun Go Down On Me'?
   Tim Rice, George Michael, Aretha Franklin

8 Which hit begins, "The road is long with many a
   winding turn"?   'Love Me For A Reason', 'Any
   Dream Will Do', 'He Aint Heavy He's My Brother'

9 Which song was a hit for Blondie in 1979?   'Manic
   Monday', 'Sunday Girl', 'Saturday Night'

10 Windsor Davies and Don Estelle had a hit with
    'Whispering Grass' and co-starred in which
    sitcom?   Dad's Army, Porridge, It Ain't Half Hot Mum

ANSWERS

1. Beyonce Knowles 2. The Moody Blues 3. The Corrs 4. Black Or White
5. Wooden horse 6. 'Spirit In The Sky' 7. George Michael 8. 'He Aint Heavy
He's My Brother' 9. 'Sunday Girl' 10. It Ain't Half Hot Mum

QUIZ 140

1. What is musophobia the morbid fear of? Men, Music, Mice

2. What meat is traditionally used in the preparation of moussaka? Lamb, Pork, Beef

3. What is the largest lake in North America? Erie, Huron, Superior

4. Bauxite is the principal ore of which metal? Tin, Lead, Aluminium

5. In which film did Clint Eastwood co-star with Jean Seberg? *Paint Your Wagon*, *Play Misty For Me*, *In The Line Of Fire*

6. In the equation $E=MC^2$, what does the C signify? Mass, Weight, Speed of light

7. What is plutophobia the fear of? Dogs, Rain, Wealth, Planets

8. In what year did Victoria Adams marry David Beckham? 1998, 1999, 2000

9. Who was the grandfather of Queen Elizabeth II? George VI, George V, Edward VIII

10. Where is the number 20 flanked by 1 and 14? Plimsoll line, Roulette wheel, Computer keyboard

ANSWERS

1. Mice 2. Lamb 3. Superior 4. Aluminium 5. *Paint Your Wagon*
6. Speed of light 7. Wealth 8. 1999 9. George V 10. Roulette wheel

QUIZ 141

1 What name is given to a race horse that has never won a race?   Maiden, Nursery, Donkey

2 Who rode a horse called Copenhagen into battle? Richard III, Robert the Bruce, Duke of Wellington

3 Who penned the novel *Black Beauty*?   Anna Sewell, Catherine Cookson, Margaret Mitchell

4 What type of horse has brown and white patches? Skewbald, Palamino, Bay

5 In show jumping, how many penalty points are incurred if a rider falls off the horse?   8, 10, 20

6 In what month is the Royal Ascot race meeting traditionally held?   April, June, September

7 Which horse scaled the heights to win the 1998 Grand National?   West Tip, Ben Nevis, Earth Summit

8 In which film did Robert Redford play Sonny Steele, a rodeo star?   *The Electric Horseman*, *The Horse Whisperer*, *The Sting*

9 Which cowboy rode a steed called Topper?   The Cisco Kid, Jesse James, Hopalong Cassidy

10 What is the name of the highest fence in the Aintree Grand National?   The Chair, The Bed, The Wardrobe

ANSWERS

1. Maiden 2. Duke of Wellington 3. Anna Sewell 4. Skewbald 5. 8 6. June
7. Earth Summit 8. *The Electric Horseman* 9. Hopalong Cassid 10. The Chair

QUIZ 142

• •

1 In what month is Burns Night celebrated in Scotland?   January, April, December

2 The Cape of Good Hope is found at the southern tip of where?   Africa, Portugal, Australia

3 Which car manufacturer has made models called the Patrol and the Serena?   Nissan, Proton, Rover

4 What is a western diamondback?   Cat, Alligator, Rattlesnake

5 What name is given to a sixteen size bottle of champagne?   Balthazar, Imperiale, Jeroboam

6 In which film, based on a Jane Austen novel, does Alan Rickman play Colonel Brandon?   *Mansfield Park, Pride and Prejudice, Sense and Sensibility*

7 Where is the mizzenmast found on a ship?   Near the front, Near the back, On the starboard

8 What is the name of Ozzy and Sharon Osbourne's oldest daughter?   Sharon, Kelly, Aimee

9 Which British city is served by Turnhouse Airport?   Edinburgh, Swansea, Bristol

10 In which country did Daimler cars originate?   Germany, Japan, France

ANSWERS

1. January 2. Africa 3. Nissan 4. Rattlesnake 5. Balthazar 6. *Sense and Sensibility* 7. Near the back 8. Aimee 9. Edinburgh 10. Germany

QUIZ 143

• •

Which film featured the characters of:

1 Virgil "the Cooler King" Hilts and Anthony "the Scrounger" Hendley? *The Great Escape, Ocean's Eleven, The Italian Job*

2 Vincent Vega and Winston "The Wolf" Wolfe? *The Deer Hunter, Pulp Fiction, Rain Man*

3 Jack Dawson and Rose De Witt? *Ghost, Sister Act, Titanic*

4 4Jor-el and Perry White? *Spiderman, Batman, Superman*

5 Ellen O'Hara and Ashley Wilkes? *All About Eve, The Great Gatsby, Gone With The Wind*

6 Maximus and Commodus? *El Cid, Gladiator, Ben Hur*

7 Rafiki and Zazu? *Aladdin, The Lion King, The Jungle Book*

8 Mr Big and Solitaire? *Live And Let Die, Diamonds Are Forever, From Russia With Love*

9 Danny Zuko and Betty Rizzo? *Fame, West Side Story, Grease*

10 Sean Archer and Castor Troy? *Face Off, Die Hard, Mission Impossible*

ANSWERS

1. *The Great Escape* 2. *Pulp Fiction* 3. *Titanic* 4. *Superman* 5. *Gone With The Wind* 6. *Gladiator* 7. *The Lion King* 8. *Live And Let Die* 9. *Grease* 10. *Face Off*

QUIZ 144

1 On a dartboard, what number is flanked by 19 and 17?   1, 3, 7

2 Which 1798 battle inspired the poem that begins, "The boy stood on the burning deck"?   Battle of Midway, Battle of Jutland, Battle of the Nile

3 What is the middle colour of a rainbow?   Green, Indigo, Red

4 Which girl band recorded the album, Always And Forever?   Spice Girls, Eternal, En Vogue

5 Who sailed in a research ship called The Calypso?   James Cook, Jacques Cousteau, Charles Darwin

6 In *The Omen* films what is the last name of the character of Damian?   Flowers, Thorn, Rose

7 Which country's flag features a Union Jack and a southern cross?   Australia, Falkland Islands, Malta

8 Which body of water forms a coastline with the East coast of Saudi Arabia?   Persian Gulf, Red Sea, Sea of Galilee

9 What type of animal is Eeyore in the Winnie The Pooh tales?   Tiger, Donkey, Rabbit

10 In which country did the Euro replace the guilder?   Albania, Belgium, Netherlands

ANSWERS

1. 3 2. Battle of the Nile 3. Green 4. Eternal 5. Jacques Cousteau 6. Thorn
7. Australia 8. Persian Gulf 9. Donkey 10. Netherlands

QUIZ 145

• •

1 Which politician penned the novel, *Cain and Abel*?
   Jeffrey Archer, John Major, Edwina Currie

2 What is the minimum age requirement for a US
   President? 25, 30, 35

3 In which palace was Winston Churchill born?
   Blenheim, Buckingham, Crystal

4 In which 1993 film did Kevin Kline play the
   President of the USA? *Dave, Jack, Nixon*

5 Which world leader died in 1989 after a 62 year
   reign? Emperor Hirohito, General Franco, Papa
   Doc Duvalier?

6 In 1984, Pierre Trudeau resigned as Prime minister
   of which country? Argentina, France, Canada

7 Which British politician featured in the video of
   the Tracy Ullman hit, 'My Guy'? Michael Foot, Neil
   Kinnock, Margaret Thatcher

8 Which dictator was shot and wounded by Violet
   Gibson? Pol Pot, Adolph Hitler, Benito Mussolini

9 Who did David Lloyd George replace as British
   Prime Minister in 1916? Stanley Baldwin, Herbert
   Asquith, Robert Peel

10 Who was the first US President to be assassinated?
    James Garfield, Abraham Lincoln, John F Kennedy

ANSWERS

1. Edwina Currie 2. 35 3. Blenheim Palace 4. *Dave* 5. Emperor Hirohito
6. Canada 7. Neil Kinnock 8.Benito Mussolini 9. Herbert Asquith
10. Abraham Lincoln

QUIZ 146

. . . .

1 What name is given to a male badger?   Boar, Bull, Dog

2 Which English seaside resort's pier was badly damaged by fire in February 2003?   Brighton, Southend On Sea, Blackpool

3 What name is given to a positive electrode? Proton, Cathode, Anode

4 In what year did seat belts in cars become compulsary in the UK?   1981, 1983, 1987

5 Over what distance did Colin Jackson win an Olympic gold medal for Great Britain?   100m, 110m, 200m

6 Which modern day country was formerly called Persia?   Iran, Turkey, Iraq

7 How is Frodo releated to Bilbo Baggins in *The Lord Of The Rings*?   Son, Brother, Nephew

8 Which fictional Harry was created by Len Deighton?   Harry Potter, Harry Palmer, Dirty Harry

9 Equity is the trade union for which profession? Actors, Pilots, Police force

10 In which country did the Inca civilisation originate?   Spain, Peru, Argentina

ANSWERS

1. Boar 2. Brighton 3. Anode 4. 1983 5. 110m 6. Iran 7. Nephew
8. Harry Palmer 9. Actors 10. Peru

QUIZ 147

- -

1 What is the name of the father of Mr Spock in Star
   Trek? T'Pau, Sarek, Data

2 Which sci-fi film features a computer called Hal
   9000? *2001 A Space Odyssey, Cocoon, The
   Phantom Menace*

3 Who was the first actor to play Dr Who on TV?
   Jon Pertwee, Peter Cushing, William Hartnell

4 What was the first word spoken by ET in the
   Spielberg film? Phone, Elliott, Home

5 Which character from the *Star Wars* films is a
   protocol droid? R2D2, Chewbacca, C3PO

6 Which planet did Arnold Schwarzenegger travel
   to from Earth in the film *Total Recall*? Venus, Mars,
   Saturn

7 Who narrated the film *Armageddon*? Charlton
   Heston, Robert Mitchum, James Caan

8 In which city was the sci-fi thriller Minority Report
   set? Toronto, Washington DC, London

9 In which city was the film *Blade Runner* set?
   Chicago, Los Angeles, San Francisco

10 Which character has been played on film by Jake
   Lloyd and Hayden Christensen? Anakin
   Skywalker, Superman, Buck Rogers

ANSWERS

1. Sarek 2. *2001 A Space Odyssey* 3. William Hartnell 4. Elliott 5. C3PO
6. Mars 7. Charlton Heston 8. Washington DC 9. Los Angeles 10. Anakin
Skywalker

QUIZ 148

1 From what animal is roquefort cheese obtained? Cow, Nanny goat, Ewe

2 How many minutes are there in a week? 10080, 20080, 30080

3 Who did Emilio Estevez portray in the film *Young Guns*? Billy the Kid, Jesse James, Doc Holliday

4 From what wood were longbows traditionally made? Sycamore, Yew, Walnut

5 Which post has been held by George Carey and William Temple? Poet Laureate, Archbishop of Canterbury, Prime Minister

6 For which film did Halle Berry win a Best Actress Oscar in 2002? *Monsters Ball*, *Die Another Day*, *Swordfish*

7 Which group did Beyonce Knowles leave? TLC, Cleopatra, Destiny's Child

8 In which resort did Billy Butlin open his first holiday camp? Scarborough, Skegness, Morecambe

9 What is the name of Andy Capp's wife? Virginia, Adelaide, Florence

10 In which century was the Dickens novel *Barnaby Rudge* set? 16th, 17th, 18th

ANSWERS

1. Ewe 2. 10080 3. Billy the Kid 4. Yew 5. Archbishop of Canterbury
6. *Monsters Ball* 7. Destiny's Child 8. Skegness 9. Florence 10. 18th

QUIZ 149

. . . .

1 What is the name of Postman Pat's wife?   Susan, Samantha, Sara

2 Who was the biblical husband of Jezebel? Doubting Thomas, King Ahab, Lazarus

3 Whose second wife was called Poppea?   Claudius, Caesar, Nero

4 Who married Marilyn Monroe in 1956?   Jim Dougherty, Joe Di Maggio, Arthur Miller,

5 Which film star married Maria Shriver, the niece of John F Kennedy?   Clint Eastwood, Paul Newman, Arnold Schwarzenegger

6 How many husbands did Scarlet O'Hara have in Gone With The Wind?   1, 3, 5

7 Which England sporting captain did Julia Smith marry in 1994?   Will Carling, David Gower, Tony Adams

8 In what year did Prince Andrew marry Sarah Ferguson?   1982, 1986, 1988

9 Who was Eva Braun married to for one day? Adolph Hitler, Buddy Holly, Glenn Miller

10 How many times did the composer Ludwig Van Beethoven marry?   None, 2, 7

ANSWERS

1. Sara 2. King Ahab 3. Nero 4. Arthur Miller 5. Arnold Schwarzenegger
6. 3 7. Will Carling 8. 1986 9. Adolph Hitler 10. None

QUIZ 150

. . . .

1 What is a Maris Piper?   Onion, Potato, Tomato

2 What is a pipistrelle?   Bat, Flower, Orange

3 What was the sub-title of the third *Star Trek* film?
   The Voyage Home, *The Undiscovered Country*, *The Search For Spock*

4 What did Vincent Van Gogh use to commit suicide?   Gun, Knife, Dynamite

5 Who are in charge in a theocracy?   Military, Trade unions, Priests

6 Who wrote the song, 'I Get A Kick Out Of You'?
   Cole Porter, Paul Anka, George Gershwin

7 Which of the following most accurately describes a person who is esurient?   Rich, Greedy, Penniless

8 What is mined using the Frasch process?   Salt, Silver, Sulphur

9 Which football club has been managed in the past by Peter Reid, Alan Ball and Joe Mercer?
   Sunderland, Portsmouth, Manchester City

10 What colour are the houses in the boardgame of Monopoly?   Green, Red, White

ANSWERS

1. Potato 2. Bat 3. *The Search For Spock* 4. Gun 5. Priests 6. Cole Porter
7. Greedy 8. Sulphur 9. Manchester City 10. Green

QUIZ 151

• •

1 What was the first thing that Old King Cole called for? Dog, Bowl, Pipe

2 What did the man in the moon burn his mouth on? Plum porridge, Boiled potato, Toasted cheese

3 In the rhyme Four And Twenty Blackbirds, whose nose was pecked off by a blackbird? The King, The maid, The knave

4 What colour are the buckles on Bobby Shafto's knees? Black, Silver, Golden

5 What type of shells did Mary Mary Quite Contrary grow in her garden? Oyster shells, Cockle shells, Sea shells

6 Who rode on a pony with a feather in his cap? Yankee Doodle Dandy, The grand Old Duke of York, Dandy Dan

7 What did the old woman who lived in a shoe feed her children? Gruel, Broth, Rice pudding

8 Who pulled Pussy out of the well? Timmy Trout, Sammy Sprout, Tommy Stout

9 Who stole barley from a baker's shop? Silly Billy, Holly Dolly, Charley Parley

10 What time was it when the mouse ran down the clock? 1 o'clock, 3 o'clock, 12 o'clock

ANSWERS

1. Pipe 2. Plum porridge 3. The maid 4. Silver 5. Cockle shells 6. Yankee Doodle Dandy 7. Broth 8. Tommy Stout 9. Charley Parley 10. 1 o'clock

QUIZ 152

- -

1 Who recorded the albums Out Of Time and Murmur?   OMD, REM, ELO

2 Which country won the Americas Cup in 2000? USA, New Zealand, Australia

3 What nationality is Lady Penelope in Thunderbirds?   American, English, Italian

4 What does the L stand for in the acronym LASER? Latitude, Light, Luminous

5 Who were England playing when David Beckham was sent off in the 1988 World Cup finals?   Brazil, Uruguay, Argentina

6 Which British river is spanned by the Erskine Bridge?   Clyde, Avon, Severn

7 Which Spice Girl topped the charts with Bag It Up?   Mel B, Mel C, Geri Halliwell

8 On which hill was the Battle of Hastings fought? Senlac Hill, Solsbury Hill, Pendle Hill

9 In which city is the Phantom Of The Opera set? Venice, Paris, Madrid

10 What does the E stand for with regard to the food additives E Numbers?   European, Even, English

ANSWERS

1. REM 2. New Zealand 3. English 4. Light (Light Amplification by Stimulated Emission of Radiation) 5. Argentina 6. Clyde 7. Geri Halliwell 8. Senlac Hill 9. Paris 10. European

QUIZ 153

- -

1 What is the last name of the character played by Ronnie Barker in *Open All Hours*? Avery, Archer, Arkwright

2 What is the name of the Royle family's local public house? The Feathers, The Swan, The Flowers

3 What role does Peter Sallis play in *Last Of The Summer Wine*? Foggy, Clegg, Seymour

4 What is the name of Basil Fawlty's wife? Prunella, Sybil, Connie

5 In which sitcom did Richard Wilson play Dr Thorpe? *Dr At Large, Only When I Laugh, A Very Peculiar Practice*

6 In which city is the Likely Lads set? London, Newcastle, Birmingham

7 Which comedy series was set in Crimpton On Sea? *One Foot In The Grave, September Song, Hi-De-Hi*

8 Which sitcom first featured Mork from Ork? *Soap, Roseanne, Happy Days*

9 What rank was held by Arthur Lowe's character in *Dad's Army*? Major, Captain, General

10 In which county is *Phoenix Nights* set? Yorkshire, Warwickshire, Lancashire

ANSWERS

1. Arkwright 2. The Feathers 3. Clegg 4. Sybil 5. *Only When I Laugh*
6. Newcastle 7. *Hi-De-Hi* 8. *Happy Days* 9. Captain 10. Lancashire

QUIZ 154

1 A labour is the collective noun for which group of animals? Moles, Monkeys, Magpies

2 Which character is voiced in *The Simpsons* by Nancy Cartwright? Lisa, Bart, Marge

3 Which US President ordered the dropping of the first atomic bomb in World War II? Franklin D Roosevelt, Dwight Eisenhower, Harry S Truman

4 What vitamin is lacking in people suffering from scurvy? K, B, C

5 What nickname completes the fighting name of heavyweight boxer James Smith? Soul Destroyer, Bone Crusher, Head Banger

6 In which seaside resort is Fawlty Towers set? Brighton, Torquay, Bournemouth

7 What is the Ukraine's capital? Tallinn, Riga, Kiev

8 Curly Neal was a member of which famous sporting team? New York Yankees, Harlem Globetrotters, San Francisco 49ers

9 What animal has species called pilot, sperm and right? Dolphin, Walrus, Whale

10 In what decade was penicillin discovered? 1920s, 1930s, 1940s

ANSWERS

1. Moles 2. Bart 3. Harry S Truman 4. C 5. Bone Crusher 6. Torquay 7. Kiev
8. Harlem Globetrotters 9. Whale 10. 1920s

QUIZ 155

• •

What is studied by a …

1 Renologist? Kidneys, Liver, Brain

2 Herpetologist? Fruit, Plants, Reptiles

3 Palaentologist? Colours, Fossils, Weather

4 Ichthyologist? Codes, Fish, Cancer

5 Hagiologist? Witchcraft, Saints, Monarchs

6 Osteologist? Bones, Flowers, Comets

7 Ornithologist? Insects, Family trees, Birds

8 Hoplologist? Weapons, Frogs, Beer

9 Myologist? Joints, Blood, Muscles

10 Petrologist? Rocks, Cats, Lizards

ANSWERS

1. Kidneys 2. Reptiles 3. Fossils 4. Fish 5. Saints 6. Bones 7. Birds
8. Weapons 9. Muscles 10. Rocks

QUIZ 156

1 What is the last letter on the bottom row of a computer keyboard? N, M, X

2 What name is given to a young kangaroo? Jimmy, Joey, Jackie

3 Who is the patron saint of children? Luke, Bernard, Nicholas

4 In the British army, what rank is directly above a colonel? Lieutenant, Brigadier, Major

5 What is the official national language of Mozambique? Portuguese, Dutch, Spanish

6 Which organ of the body contains insulin? Spleen, Pancreas, Kidney

7 What does the M stand for with regard to MG cars? Mercedes, Morris, Mitsubishi

8 What did the B stand for in the name of the former US President Lyndon B Johnson? Byron, Baines, Bradley

9 In which cult TV series was Laura Palmer murdered? *24*, *Twin Peaks*, *Six Feet Under*

10 In 2003, at which venue was the British Formula One Grand Prix held? Aintree, Silverstone, Brands Hatch

ANSWERS

1. M 2. Joey 3. Nicholas 4. Brigadier 5. Portuguese 6. Pancreas 7. Morris
8. Baines 9. *Twin Peaks* 10. Silverstone

QUIZ 157

- -

1 Who gave Harry Potter his lightning scar? Hagrid, Voldemort, Snape

2 In which country is the Shakespeare play *Hamlet* set? Denmark, Austria, Italy

3 Which animals took control of the farm in Animal Farm? Dogs, Pigs, Cows

4 In which school is Tom Brown's Schooldays set? Eton, Rugby, Harvard

5 The film *The Slipper And The Rose* is based on which fairytale? *Sleeping Beauty*, *Cinderella*, *Thumbelina*

6 Which land was visited by four children called Peter, Edmund, Susan and Lucy? Oz, Middle Earth, Narnia

7 'Down The Rabbit Hole' is the first chapter of which novel? *Alice's Adventures In Wonderland*, *The Hobbit*, *The Borrowers*

8 What is David Cornwell's pen name? Mark Twain, John Le Carre, George Orwell

9 What did Charles Dickens refer to as a "London particular"? Fog, Lord Mayor, Train

10 Which classic novel is set in a house called Manderley? *Wuthering Heights*, *Emma*, *Rebecca*

ANSWERS

1. Voldemort 2. Denmark 3. Pigs 4. Rugby 5. *Cinderella* 6. Narnia
7. *Alice's Adventures In Wonderland* 8. John Le Carre 9 Fog 10. *Rebecca*

QUIZ 158

• •

1 What was the former name of New York?   New Paris, New Amsterdam, New Castle

2 What sport is played by the San Francisco Giants? Ice Hockey, Baseball, Basketball

3 Who played the role of Charlie Hinton in the 2003 comedy film, *Daddy Day Care*?   Jackie Chan, Eddie Murphy, Adam Sandler

4 How is 2000 written in Roman numerals?   MM, DD, CC

5 What rank was Tom Parker, the manager of Elvis Presley?   Major, Colonel, General

6 In which country is the most westerly point of mainland Europe?   Portugal, Germany, Denmark

7 In which film did Robin Williams provide the voice of Dr Know?   *Jumanji, A.I., Aladdin*

8 What does the T stand for with regard to the airport abbreviation ATC?   Time, Terminal, Traffic

9 What is the first name of Tom Sawyer's girlfriend? Belinda, Barbara, Becky

10 What is crossed with a grapefruit to make an ugli fruit?   Tangerine, Pineapple, Plum

ANSWERS

1. New Amsterdam 2. Baseball 3. Eddie Murphy 4. MM 5. Colonel
6. Portugal 7. *A.I.* 8. Traffic 9. Becky 10. Tangerine

QUIZ 159

1. What is the chief constituent of the air that we breathe? Carbon dioxide, Nitrogen, Oxygen

2. What is combined with copper to make brass? Iron, Tin, Zinc

3. What does a Geiger counter measure? Speed, Weight, Radioactivity

4. Which inert gas has the atomic number of 2? Xenon, Helium, Radon

5. If a person is suffering from dysphagia, what do they have difficulty in doing? Swallowing, Reading, Hearing

6. What is the lightest known metal? Barium, Aluminium, Lithium

7. Which part of the human body is affected by nephritis? Lungs, Brain, Kidneys

8. Which gas propels a cork from a champagne bottle? Carbon dioxide, Methane, Ammonia

9. What condition is caused by a shortage of haemoglobin? Anaemia, Epilepsy, Gout

10. Approximately 70% of the sun comprises of what? Neon, Helium, Hydrogen

ANSWERS

1. Nitrogen 2. Zinc 3. Radioactivity 4. Helium 5. Swallowing 6. Lithium
7. Kidneys 8. Carbon dioxide 9. Anaemia 10. Hydrogen

QUIZ 160

. . . .

1 Which pantomime features the character of Buttons? Cinderella, Mother Goose, Aladdin

2 The island group, the Azores, belong to which country? Tunisia, Ecuador, Portugal

3 What animal features on the logo of Bacardi bottles? Horse, Bat, Cat

4 What is the better known name of Edward Bear? Boo Boo, Winnie The Pooh, Paddington Bear

5 Who is the central character of Homer's the *Iliad*? Achilles, Hercules, Helen of Troy

6 The ELO system rates the top players in which game? Darts, Chess, Bridge

7 What is the collective noun for a group of monkeys? Chatter, Troop, Army

8 Which river flows into the North Sea at Sunderland? Tyne, Wear, Clyde

9 Which New York intersection do Broadway, Seventh Avenue and 42nd Street form? Madison Square, Wall Street, Times Square

10 Which singer penned an autobiography entitled, Take Me Home? Noddy Holder, John Denver, Olivia Newton John

ANSWERS

1. Cinderella 2. Portugal 3. Bat 4. Winnie The Pooh 5. Achilles 6. Chess
7. Troop 8. Wear 9. Times Square 10. John Denver

QUIZ 161

• •

1 What nickname was given to landscape gardener Lancelot Brown?   Greenfingers, Capability, Planter

2 What was the nickname of the classical composer Antonio Vivaldi?   The Black Knight, The Red Priest, The Scarlet Prince

3 Which sportsman is nicknamed The Long Fellow? Meadowlark Lemon, Lennox Lewis, Lester Piggott

4 What is nicknamed the Garden Resort of Wales? Llandudno, Rhyl, Conway, Colwyn Bay

5 Which King of England was nicknamed Lackland? Henry 1, King John, Charles 1

6 What is the nickname of Scunthorpe United FC? The Steelmen, The Copper Boys, The Irons

7 What nickname was given to King George III? Sailor George, Soldier George, Farmer George

8 What nickname was bestowed upon the world champion boxer Thomas Hearns?   Hit Man, Cinderella Man, Invisible Man

9 By what name was Charles Sherwood Stratton better known?   Tom Thumb, Champagne Charlie, Bonnie Prince Charlie

10 Which singer was nicknamed the Man In Black? Alvin Stardust, Johnny Cash, Ozzy Osbourne

ANSWERS

1. Capability 2. The Red Priest 3. Lester Piggott 4. Colwyn Bay 5. King John
6. The Irons 7. Farmer George 8. Hit Man 9. Tom Thumb 10. Johnny Cash

QUIZ 162

• •

1 The adjective taurine refers to which animal?
   Owl, Tiger, Bull

2 What was the destination of Geoffrey Chaucer's
   pilgrims? Jerusalem, Avalon, Canterbury

3 Which river runs alongside the Luxor Temple?
   Nile, Ganges, Mekong

4 What has been the nationality of the majority of
   Popes? Greek, Polish, Italian

5 What does a dromophobic person fear?
   Speaking in public, Flying, Crossing the road

6 What is the name of the official residence of the
   President of France? Notre Dame, Eiffel Tower,
   Elysee Palace

7 Which dictator founded the Khmer Rouge? Pol
   Pot, General Galtieri, General Pinochet

8 What is the first animal mentioned in the nursery
   rhyme, Hey Diddle Diddle? Cat, Dog, Cow

9 Who won an Oscar as Best Director for the film
   The Pianist? Martin Scorsese, Roman Polanski,
   Milos Forman

10 Which car manufacturer made the DB series of
   models? Porsche, Rolls Royce, Aston Martin

ANSWERS

1. Bull 2. Canterbury 3. Nile 4. Italian 5. Crossing the road 6. Elysee Palace
7. Pol Pot 8. Cat 9. Roman Polanski 10. Aston Martin

QUIZ 163

1 In which county is Stonehenge? Staffordshire, Lancashire, Wiltshire

2 What name is given to an inhabitant of the Orkneys? Orkon, Orcadian, Orcostan

3 Where is the University of East Anglia located? Lowestoft, Norwich, Felixstowe

4 What is the name of the tower that houses Big Ben? St Peters, St Georges, St Stephens

5 What is the longest river in Scotland? Clyde, Perth, Tay

6 In 1993, the football manager Brian Clough was granted the freedom of which city? Nottingham, London, York

7 Which city is served by Aldegrove Airport? Swansea, Belfast, Southampton

8 Which 1995 film starring Ted Danson was set in Scotland? *Braveheart*, *Loch Ness*, *Local Hero*

9 To which saint is Westminster Abbey dedicated? St Bernard, St Peter, St Nicholas

10 In which county did John Constable set his painting, The Haywain? Devon, Cumbria, Suffolk

ANSWERS

1. Wiltshire 2. Orcadian 3. Norwich 4. St Stephens 5. Tay 6. Nottingham
7. Belfast 8. *Loch Ness* 9. St Peter 10. Suffolk

QUIZ 164

1 In which country is the Southern Alps mountain range?   Italy, New Zealand, Chile

2 Who was the first European to sail around the Cape of Good Hope?   Francis Drake, Vasco de Gama, Ferdinand Magellan

3 What is the fruity nickname of New York?   The Big Pear, The Big Apple, The Big Orange

4 Sherman and Cromwell are both types of what?   Trumpet, Tree, Tank

5 Barajas Airport serves which European capital city?   Lisbon, Bratislava, Madrid

6 What item of wear provided the nickname of the Kray twins associate Jack McVitie?   Shoe, Suit, Hat

7 Which European nation has been ruled by the House of Orange?   Netherlands, Spain, Belgium

8 Which season is known as the Fall in the USA?   Spring, Autumn, Winter

9 What type of bird is a Beltsville?   Turkey, Duck, Pheasant

10 Which TV series featured a robotic dog called K9?   *Lost In Space, Star Trek, Dr Who*

ANSWERS

1. New Zealand 2. Vasco de Gama 3. The Big Apple 4. Tank 5. Madrid
6. Hat 7. Netherlands 8. Autumn 9. Turkey 10. *Dr Who*

QUIZ 165

1. On which album did Tom Jones collaborate with numerous top stars including Robbie Williams and The Cardigans?   Refire, Reload, Replay

2. Who won the award for Best British Group at the 2002 Brit Awards?   Blur, Travis, Coldplay

3. Which Irish group first had five number one hit singles in the UK?   U2, Boyzone, Westlife

4. Ray Dorset provided lead vocals for which chart topping band of the 1970s?   Hot Chocolate, Mungo Jerry, Wizzard

5. Which album was released by Madonna in 1997? Ray Of Light, The Immaculate Collection, Music

6. Which pop duo had a 1985 hit with 'We Close Our Eyes'?   Go North, Go West, Go South

7. What was Wham's first number one?   Wham Rap, Wake Me Up Before You Go Go, Bad Boys,

8. Which duo had hits with 'Crying In The Rain' and 'When Will I Be Loved'?   Simon & Garfunkel, The Proclaimers, Everly Brothers

9. Which U2 hit was a tribute to Billie Holliday? 'With Or Without You', 'Desire', 'Angel Of Harlem'

10. What was the name of Gary Puckett's backing band?   The Union Gap, The Strawbs, The Deltones

ANSWERS

1. Reload 2. Travis 3. Boyzone 4. Mungo Jerry 5. Ray Of Light 6. Go West
7. Wake Me Up Before You Go Go 8. Everly Brothers 9. 'Angel Of Harlem'
10. The Union Gap

QUIZ 166

1 On which river does the city of Rangoon lie?
Irawaddy, Niger, Congo

2 Valencia Island lies off the coast of which country?
Spain, Ireland, South Africa

3 Which TV series featured four brothers called Joey,
Jack, Billy and Adrian? *Brookside*, *Bread*,
Thunderbirds

4 How many lines comprise a sonnet? 8, 14, 16

5 What is the first name of the character played by
Kiefer Sutherland in the TV drama *24*? Jez, Jim,
Jack

6 Which building did the Bond villain Goldfinger
attempt to rob? Fort Knox, Taj Mahal, Louvre

7 For which football league club did Peter Shilton
make his league debut? Leicester City, Stoke City,
Notts County

8 What flavour are fennel leaves? Vanilla, Mint,
Aniseed

9 Thermidor is an old name for which month of the
year? June, July, August

10 Which capital is served by Collinstown Airport?
Dublin, Belfast, Edinburgh

ANSWERS

1. Irawaddy 2. Ireland 3. *Bread* 4. 14 5. Jack 6. Fort Knox 7. Leicester City
8. Aniseed 9. August 10. Dublin

QUIZ 167

1 Which state of the USA was named after the wife of Charles I?   Maryland, Virginia, North Carolina

2 Which state of the USA is known as the Beehive State?   North Dakota, New Hampshire, Utah

3 WI is the zip code of which state?   Wisconsin, West Virginia, Washington

4 What is known as the Sooner State? Delaware, Oklahoma, Tennessee

5 From which country did the USA buy Alaska? United Kingdom, Spain, Russia

6 Harrisburg is the state capital of which state? Ohio, Idaho, Pennsylvania

7 Which animal provides the nickname of Michigan?   Wolverine, Mustang, Pelican

8 How many states of the USA have just four letters in their name?   3, 4, 5

9 Boston is the state capital of which state? Massachusetts, Vermont, New Jersey

10 What does the DC stand for in the name of Washington DC?   District of Columbia, Diamond Centennial, Democratic Congress

ANSWERS

1. Maryland 2. Utah 3. Wisconsin 4. Oklahoma 5. Russia 6. Pennsylvania
7. Wolverine 8. 3 9. Massachusetts 10. District of Columbia

QUIZ 168

• •

1 Who penned the novel *The Bonfire Of The Vanities*?
   Tom Lambe, Tom Wolfe, Tom Rabbite

2 Bob Hawke was the Prime Minister of which
   country in the 1980s? Canada, Australia, New
   Zealand

3 What commodity is associated with Mincing Lane
   in London? Meat, Tea, Clothes

4 What type of racing takes place at Santa Pod?
   Drag, Greyhound, Cycle

5 How many rooms are there in the board game of
   Cluedo? 8, 9, 10

6 What girls name is found at the end of a bell
   rope? Lucy, Jenny, Sally

7 Which state of the USA is known as the Last
   Frontier? Alaska, Colorado, New Mexico

8 What is the alternative name for the marsh
   marigold? Queencup, Earlcup, Kingcup

9 What is used to play a vibraphone? Plectrum,
   Hammers, Bow

10 La Guardia Airport in New York is named after a
   former what? Mayor, General, Film star

ANSWERS

1. Tom Wolfe 2. Australia 3. Tea 4. Drag racing 5. 9 6. Sally 7. Alaska
8. Kingcup 9. Hammers 10. Mayor

QUIZ 169

• •

In what year…

1 Was the Berlin Wall erected?   1941, 1951, 1961

2 Did Lady Astor become the first female MP in the
   House of Commons?   1899, 1919, 1929

3 Was the FA Cup final known as The Matthews
   Final?   1951, 1953, 1957

4 Did King Edward VIII abdicate?   1935, 1936, 1939

5 Did Princess Anne become the Princess Royal?
   1983, 1985, 1987

6 Did the Barings Bank collapse?   1995, 1996, 2000

7 Did the Boston Tea Party take place?   1743, 1763,
   1773

8 Did Bob Geldof receive an honourary
   knighthood?   1986, 1990, 1996

9 Did The General Strike take place in Great Britain?
   1919, 1926, 1933

10 Was Tony Blair born?   1951, 1952, 1953

ANSWERS

QUIZ 170

• •

1 Yaphet Kotto played the villain of the piece in which Bond film? *Octopussy, Live And Let Die, For Your Eyes Only*

2 What is the name of Roger Rabbit's wife? Bunty, Cottontail, Jessica

3 Which US state grows the most pineapples? Florida, California, New Jersey

4 What is the oldest golf course in Great Britain? St Andrews, Troon, Wentworth

5 Which member of The Monkees, starred as a child actor in the TV series *Circus Boy*? Peter Tork, Mike Nesmith, Mickey Dolenz

6 Where does the Ceremony Of The Keys take place in London? House Of Lords, Tower Of London, Big Ben

7 In what year was Pope John Paul II elected? 1976, 1978, 1980

8 On which island is Mount Etna? Capri, Sicily, Elba

9 Which US TV series featured two families called the Tates and the Campbells? *Soap, Dallas, Dynasty*

10 Who played in his sixth FA Cup final in 2004? Ryan Giggs, Roy Keane, Gary Neville

ANSWERS

1. *Live And Let Die* 2. Jessica 3. Florida 4. St Andrews 5. Mickey Dolenz
6. Tower Of London 7. 1978 8. Sicily 9. *Soap* 10. Roy Keane

QUIZ 171

. . . .

1 What type of birds are the cartoon creatures Heckle and Jeckle?   Vultures, Magpies, Canaries

2 What was Disney's second full length animated film?   *Bambi, Dumbo, Pinocchio*

3 What kind of animal is Pepe le Pew?   Racoon, Skunk, Rabbit

4 In which US animated series is Hank married to Peggy?   *South Park, The Simpsons, King Of The Hill*

5 What is the name of Barney Rubble's wife in The Flintstones?   Betty, Barbara, Bertha

6 What title is held by the archenemy of Dangermouse?   Baron, Sultan, General

7 Which character in *Scooby Doo* wears spectacles?   Fred, Velma, Daphne

8 In which country did the cartoon character of Tin Tin originate?   USA, Belgium, Sweden

9 Which mouse is the best friend of Disney's flying elephant Dumbo?   Timothy, Mickey, Pixie

10 Who heads the Springfield police force in The Simpsons?   Ned Flanders, Barney Gumble, Clancy Wiggum

ANSWERS

1. Magpies 2. *Pinocchio* 3. Skunk 4. *King Of The Hill* 5. Betty 6. Baron
7. Velma 8. Belgium 9. Timothy 10. Clancy Wiggum

QUIZ 172

- -

1 On which river does the city of Cologne stand?
   Rhine, Danube, Vistula

2 Which Dickens novel was set against the French
   Revolution? *Hard Times*, *A Tale Of Two Cities*,
   The Pickwick Papers

3 In the TV series *Minder*, what is Arthur Daley's
   favourite drink? Vodka and tonic, Whisky and
   ginger, Rum and coke

4 In what month of the year does All Saints Day fall?
   April, May, November

5 Who retained his European Footballer of the Year
   Award in 1979? Michel Platini, Kevin Keegan, Ian
   Rush

6 What is the correct way to address a cardinal?
   Your Eminence, Your Worship, Father

7 What was the first name of Humphrey Bogart's
   character in *Casablanca*? Sam, Rick, Simon

8 What nationality is the novelist Umberto Eco?
   Danish, Dutch, Italian

9 What type of marine creature is an argonaut?
   Seal, Swordfish, Octopus

10 Spandau is a suburb of which German city?
   Berlin, Munich, Stuttgart

ANSWERS

1. Rhine 2. *A Tale Of Two Cities* 3. Vodka and tonic 4. November 5. Kevin
Keegan 6. Your Eminence 7. Rick 8. Italian 9. Octopus 10. Berlin

QUIZ 173

1 Which Gilbert & Sullivan opera is sub-titled The Slave Of Duty?   HMS Pinafore, The Pirates Of Penzance, The Mikado

2 What does the musical instruction fortissimo signify?   Very loud, Very fast, Plucked

3 In which city was the Halle Orchestra founded in 1857?   Manchester, London, Vienna

4 Who sang 'Forever In Blue Jeans' and 'Song Sung Blue'?   Neil Young, Paul Young, Neil Diamond

5 Which musical instrument was Glenn Miller known for playing?   Violin, Trombone, Harp

6 What does the V stand for with regard to the record label HMV?   Voice, Video, Vogue

7 What name is given to the music that opens an opera?   Overture, Opus, Libretto

8 Who recorded the song, 'Search For A Hero', used in TV adverts for Peugeot cars?   Bonnie Tyler, Meat Loaf, M People

9 In which country was the composer Mozart born? Poland, France, Austria

10 Which country provided the title of a hit record for the Human League in 1984?   Cambodia, Lebanon, Australia

ANSWERS

1. The Pirates Of Penzance 2. Very loud 3. Manchester 4. Neil Diamond
5. Trombone 6. Voice 7. Overture 8. M People 9. Austria 10. Lebanon

QUIZ 174

. . . .

1. The Scilly Isles are part of which British county? Devon, Kent, Cornwall

2. What name is given to the tail of a fox? Scut, Brush, Fan

3. Which film certification was introduced in 1950? X, PG, U

4. What is stored in the binnacle of a ship? Life boats, Compass, Telescope

5. What colour is cayenne pepper? White, Brown, Red

6. Which *Jungle Book* character was 'King Of The Swingers'? Mowgli, Dizzy, Louie

7. In which country did the fez hat originate? Morocco, Syria, Saudi Arabia

8. Which football club were crowned Division One champions in England in the 2003/04 season? Crystal Palace, Norwich City, West Ham United

9. Who was the first person to be buried in Poets Corner? Shakespeare, Byron, Chaucer

10. Which fictional comic strip character was billed as "The pilot of the future"? Flash Gordon, Dan Dare, Buck Rogers

ANSWERS

1. Cornwall 2. Brush 3. X 4. Compass 5. Red 6. Louie 7. Morocco
8. Norwich City 9. Geoffrey Chaucer 10. Dan Dare

QUIZ 175

1 What is androphobia the fear of?   Men, Children, Animals

2 What weapon was named after the French word for pomegranate?   Bazooka, Dynamite, Grenade

3 What is measured in quires?   Paper, Oil, Tea

4 What does the word zodiac literally mean?   Circle of animals, Circle of stars, Circle of months

5 In a castle, what name is given to a tower situated near the entrance gate?   Keep, Bailey, Barbican

6 Rearmouse was an old name for which animal? Hamster, Bat, Rat

7 The adjective costal refers to which part of the body?   Ribs, Lungs, Feet

8 What drink is named after the German meaning, "to store"?   Brandy, Cider, Lager

9 What name is given to the highest point of a triangle?   Atrium, Apex, Axiom

10 What part of the body is protected by a beaver on a suit of armour?   Chin, Knee, Shoulder

ANSWERS

1. Men 2. Grenade 3. Paper 4. Circle of animals 5. Barbican 6. Bat 7. Ribs
8. Lager 9. Apex 10. Chin

QUIZ 176

. . . .

1 Which British Royal competed in the 1976 Olympic Games? Prince Charles, Princess Anne, Prince Andrew

2 Which age followed the Stone Age? Ice Age, Bronze Age, Iron Age

3 What is the name of Bill and Hillary Clinton's daughter? Carling, Chelsea, Candice

4 What does the P stand for in the computer abbreviation CPU? Processing, Pixel, Paste

5 Which dog provided the name of the research ship of Charles Darwin? Terrier, Mastiff, Beagle

6 What was the middle name of Lady Diana Spencer? Lydia, Caroline, Frances

7 The US comedy series *Spin City* is set in which city? Philadelphia, New York, Pittsburgh

8 Which king awarded the first George Cross? George III, George V, George VI

9 In which decade was the charity organisation Oxfam founded? 1920s, 1940s, 1960s

10 Which cartoon character conducted the orchestra in the 1940 film *Fantasia*? Betty Boop, Felix the Cat, Mickey Mouse

ANSWERS

1. Princess Anne 2. Bronze Age 3. Chelsea 4. Processing 5. Beagle
6. Frances 7. New York 8. George VI 9. 1940s 10. Mickey Mouse

QUIZ 177

• •

1 What was ceded to Britain under the 1842 Treaty of Nanking?   Hong Kong, India, Gibraltar

2 Which century witnessed the Gunpowder Plot? 15th, 16th, 17th

3 Which British monarch was known as, Sailor George?   George II, George IV, George V

4 Which US President shares his surname with the highest mountain of North America?   Fillmore, McKinley, Lincoln

5 Who signed The Pact Of Steel with Hitler in 1939? Stalin, Himmler, Mussolini

6 What calendar was adopted by Britain in 1752? Gregorian, Julian, Roman

7 In 1991, whose statue was removed from Moscow's Red Square?   Rasputin, Gagarin, Lenin

8 Which monarch was beheaded in January 1649? Charles I, James I, James II

9 Who led the Dam Busters raid in World War II? Douglas Bader, Bomber Harris, Guy Gibson

10 Where did the Iron Duke defeat the Man of Destiny?   Trafalgar, Waterloo, Little Big Horn

ANSWERS

1. Hong Kong 2. 17th 3. George V 4. McKinley 5. Mussolini 6. Gregorian
7. Lenin 8. Charles I 9. Guy Gibson 10. Waterloo

QUIZ 178

- -

1 In which country did acupuncture originate?
China, USA, Malaysia

2 What was the name of Abraham Lincoln's wife?
Laura, Anne, Mary

3 Which car manufacturer has made models called
the Mustang and the Probe?   Audi, BMW, Ford

4 Salsa is the Spanish word for what?   Hot, Sauce,
Salt

5 What is the first name of the literary detective
Inspector Maigret?   Pierre, Jules, Yves

6 What did the second S stand for with regard to
the USSR?   Soviet, Socialist, Stalinism

7 The motto of the FBI is Fidelity, Bravery and what?
Intuition, Integrity, Independence

8 What title is given to the wife of an earl?   Dame,
Princess, Countess

9 In what type of car was James Dean killed?
Bentley, Porsche, Cadillac

10 Which group topped the singles charts in 1983
with the song 'Candy Girl'? New Seekers, New
Edition, New Order

ANSWERS

1. China 2. Mary 3. Ford 4. Sauce 5. Jules 6. Socialist 7. Integrity
8. Countess 9. Porsche 10. New Edition

QUIZ 179

• •

1 Where in the human body are the vestibules of the semi-circular canals located?   Brain, Heart, Ear

2 What is the largest internal organ of the human body?   Spleen, Lung, Liver

3 What are there 33 of in the human body? Vertebrae, Ribs, Ligaments

4 Where are the bones known as the metacarpals found?   Skull, Ankle, Wrist

5 What is the most common blood group?   O, A, AB

6 Where in the body is the deltoid muscle?   Calf, Stomach, Shoulder

7 What is the more common name for the tympanic membrane?   Cornea, Uterus, Ear drum

8 Which part of the body is affected by gingivitis? Eyes, Skin, Gums

9 What name is given to the liquid part of the blood?   Serum, Plasma, Humour

10 What is the more common name for the disease pertussis?   Mumps, Whooping cough, German measles

ANSWERS

QUIZ 180

1 What shape are the honeycombs of bees?
   Triangular, Hexagonal, Octagonal

2 What is the word hi-fi short for?   High fidelity,
   High fives, High filament

3 Who was the first presenter of the TV talent show
   Stars In Their Eyes?   Leslie Crowther, Russ Abbot,
   Matthew Kelly

4 What is the Spanish equivalent of the word
   Mister?   Dan, Son, Don, San

5 What is the Speaker's seat in the House of Lords
   called?   Woolsack, Black Rod, Front Bench

6 In which US state was the American Indian chief
   Geronimo born?   Oklahoma, Montana, Arizona

7 Which newspaper employs Lois Lane as a
   reporter?   *Daily Globe*, *Daily Bugle*, *Daily Planet*

8 Which vesel was captained by Edward J Smith?
   Mayflower, Titanic, Marie Celeste

9 Who did Julia Roberts play in the film *Hook*?
   Wendy, Tinkerbell, Tiger Lily

10 Which nursery rhyme ends with the words, We all
   fall down?   Jack And Jill, Ring-A-Ring-A-Roses,
   Jack Be Nimble

ANSWERS

1. Hexagonal 2. High fidelity 3. Leslie Crowther 4. Don 5. Woolsack
6. Arizona 7. *Daily Planet* 8. Titanic 9. Tinkerbell 10. Ring-A-Ring-A-Roses

QUIZ 181

- -

1 What are the corns in corned beef? Sugar, Vinegar, Salt

2 On an Indian restaurant menu, what are aloo? Bread rolls, Potatoes, Bananas

3 What is the chief ingredient of chow mein? Rice, Bean sprouts, Noodles

4 What spirit provides the base of a Harvey Wallbanger cocktail? Gin, Whisky, Vodka

5 How is the Chinese gooseberry otherwise known? Passion fruit, Kiwi fruit, Grapefruit

6 What foodstuff completes the name of the dragon companion of the Clangers? Meat, Plum, Soup

7 What common food item has a name that literally means, baked twice? Cake, Biscuit, Cornflake

8 Kirsch brandy is distilled from which fruit? Apple, Pomegranate, Cherry

9 Vanilla is extracted from which plant? Orchid, Poppy, Crocus

10 In which country did satsumas originate? Spain, Brazil, Japan

ANSWERS

1. Salt 2. Potatoes 3. Noodles 4. Vodka 5. Kiwi fruit 6. Soup 7. Biscuit
8. Cherry 9. Orchid 10. Japan

QUIZ 182

1 What is the capital of Sicily? Nice, Palermo, Bonn

2 Which member of The Beatles founded the Dark Horse record label? John Lennon, Ringo Starr, George Harrison

3 In 2004, Graeme Dott was the beaten finalist in the world championships of which sport? Judo, Snooker, Table tennis

4 In which novel did Jan Valjean receive a prison sentence? *The Prisoner Of Zenda*, *Les Miserables*, *The Third Man*

5 What is the tenth consonant of the alphabet? M, N, P

6 What type of animal was Ramsbottom in The Sooty Show? Panda, Snake, Crocodile

7 Whose portrait was depicted on a Penny Black stamp? Queen Victoria, Prince Albert, George III

8 Who is the first woman to be mentioned in the Bible? Mary, Eve, Ruth

9 Which African country witnessed the Mau Mau rebellion? Kenya, Libya, Syria

10 In which country was Marie Antoinette born? France, Germany, Austria

ANSWERS

1. Palermo 2. George Harrison 3. Snooker 4. *Les Miserables* 5. M 6. Snake 7. Queen Victoria 8. Eve 9. Kenya 10. Austria

QUIZ 183

1. Llamas are native to which continent? South America, Asia, Africa

2. A shrewdness is the collective noun for which animal? Fox, Ape, Sloth

3. What name is given to a young squirrel? Puppy, Calf, Kitten

4. Which feline creation of TS Eliot is known as, The Theatre Cat? Macavity, Gus, Mungo Jerry

5. From which creature is cashmere wool obtained? Rabbit, Badger, Goat

6. What is the name of Kermit the Frog's nephew? Roland, Robin, Kevin

7. What name is given to the pupa of a butterfly? Cocoon, Larva, Chrysalis

8. What is the nickname of Derby County FC? The Hornets, The Rams, The Cockerels

9. What is the collective noun for a group of leopards? Launch, Leap, Spot

10. Which bear lives in Nutwood? Yogi Bear, Rupert the Bear, Barney Bear

ANSWERS

1. South America 2. Ape 3. Kitten 4. Gus 5. Goat 6. Robin 7. Chrysalis
8. The Rams 9. Leap 10. Rupert the Bear

QUIZ 184

1 In what decade was Neptune discovered? 1820s, 1840s, 1880s

2 Which animated film features the song, 'Some Day My Prince Will Come'? *Snow White And The Seven Dwarfs*, *Shrek*, *Sleeping Beauty*

3 What does the I stand for with regard to a bank PIN number? Identification, Issue, Investment

4 Who ended the 48 fight unbeaten run of the boxer Larry Holmes? Tony Tucker, Michael Spinks, Evander Holyfield

5 What is the transparent layer at the front of the eyeball called? Retina, Lens, Cornea

6 In which German city was the first series of *Auf Wiedersehen Pet* set? Cologne, Berlin, Dusseldorf

7 In the Rockie Mountains, what is a chinook? Mountain goat, Wind, Cave

8 Which Shakespeare character said, "If you prick us do we not bleed?"? Macbeth, Shylock, King Lear

9 What is the name of an elephant in the Winnie The Pooh tales? Babar, Heffalump, Tusker

10 Which novel by Ira Levin was adapted into a film starring Mia Farrow? *Avalanche*, *Rosemary's Baby*, *The Great Gatsby*

ANSWERS

1. 1840s 2. *Snow White And The Seven Dwarfs* 3. Identification (Personal Identification Number) 4. Michael Spinks 5. Cornea 6. Dusseldorf 7. Wind 8. Shylock 9. Heffalump 10. *Rosemary's Baby*

QUIZ 185

- -

1 What is the state capital of Oregon? Boston, Salem, Austin

2 Which river flows through Pisa and Florence? Po, Rhone, Arno

3 Which country is sometimes referred to as, The Roof of the World? Peru, Tibet, Switzerland

4 Which Canadian province incorporates the cross of St Andrew in its flag? Alberta, Ontario, Nova Scotia

5 What sea lies between Australia and New Zealand? Tasman Sea, Cook Sea, Yellow Sea

6 Which confection is associated with the French town of Montelimar? Nougat, Caramel, Marzipan

7 On which lake does the city of Milwaukee stand? Erie, Michigan, Huron

8 Where is the world's oldest casino? Las Vegas, Monte Carlo, Cairo

9 Which country is jointly ruled by the President of France and the Spanish Bishop of Urgel? Monaco, Albania, Andorra

10 What is the most westerly capital city on mainland Europe? Lisbon, Paris, Brussels

ANSWERS

1. Salem 2. Arno 3. Tibet 4. Nova Scotia 5. Tasman Sea 6. Nougat
7. Michigan 8. Monte Carlo 9. Andorra 10. Lisbon

QUIZ 186

• •

1 Which city is served by Leonardo da Vinci Airport? Nice, Rome, Naples

2 In which century was the dodo declared extinct? 15th, 17th, 19th

3 What was the first number one hit for the pop group Queen? 'Innuendo', 'Bohemian Rhapsody', 'Killer Queen'

4 At which sporting venue can spectators sit in the Warner Stand? Silverstone, Lord's, Twickenham

5 What is the correct abbreviation for the word abbreviation? Abbr, Abb, Ab

6 Which country boasts the worlds longest coastline? Brazil, Canada, Russia

7 Which novel features the line, "Four legs good, two legs bad"? *Animal Farm*, *Born Free*, *Emma*

8 Which three words complete the saying, The hand that rocks the cradle …? Rules the world, Holds the future, Keeps the faith

9 What is Sergeant Lewis' first name in the *Inspector Morse* novels? Richard, Ryan, Robbie

10 What type of footwear are sabots? Clogs, Socks, Plimsolls

ANSWERS

1. Rome 2. 17th 3. 'Bohemian Rhapsody' 4. Lord's 5. Abbr 6. Canada
7. *Animal Farm* 8. Rules the world 9. Robbie 10. Clogs

QUIZ 187

1. What was the first name of Harold Wilson?
   Matthew, James, Mark

2. Who was the first footballer to win 100 caps for
   England? Billy Wright, Peter Shilton, Bobby Moore

3. Who was the oldest of The Goons? Peter Sellers,
   Spike Milligan, Michael Bentine

4. Who survived a kidnap attempt in Gatcombe Park
   in 1974? Queen Elizabeth II, Princess Anne,
   Prince Edward

5. Who died in 399 BC, following a fatal dose of
   hemlock? Socrates, Archimedes, Hannibal

6. Who resigned as England rugby union captain in
   1996? Rory Underwood, Will Carling, Rob Andrew

7. What was the first name of the fashion designer
   Coco Chanel? Gertrude, Gabrielle, Greta

8. Which classical composer was nicknamed The
   Poet of the Piano? Brahms, Chopin, Schubert

9. Who was known as The King of the Wild Frontier?
   Davy Crockett, Kit Carson, General George Custer

10. What was the surname of the man who invented
    the revolver? Colt, Magnum, Walther

ANSWERS

1. James 2. Billy Wright 3. Spike Milligan 4. Princess Anne 5. Socrates
6. Will Carling 7. Gabrielle 8. Chopin 9. Davy Crockett 10. Colt

QUIZ 188

• •

1 What is Professor Dumbledore's first name in the *Harry Potter* novels?   Albus, Bilbo, Severus

2 How many cards comprise a pack of tarot cards? 78, 99, 108

3 Who plays the Greek hero Achilles in the 2004 film *Troy*?   Brad Pitt, Mark Wahlberg, Johnny Depp

4 Which hormone controls the levels of blood sugar?   Oestrogen, Insulin, Nandrolene

5 What is the name of the central family in the novel *Peter Pan*?   Sweet, Darling, Love

6 Jasmine and long grain are both varieties of what?   Tea, Spaghetti, Rice

7 Which British daily newspaper became a tabloid in 1971?   *Daily Mirror*, *Daily Mail*, *Sun*

8 Which musical instrument has a name that literally means, bell play?   Glockenspiel, Xylophone, Dulcimer

9 Which century witnessed the Irish Potato Famine? 13th, 15th, 19th

10 Which creature has a name that means terrible lizard?   Crocodile, Dinosaur, Alligator

ANSWERS

1. Albus 2. 78 3. Brad Pitt 4. Insulin 5. Darling 6. Rice 7. *Daily Mail*
8. Glockenspiel 9. 19th 10. Dinosaur

QUIZ 189

• •

1 Which river is nicknamed Old Muddy? Thames, Rhine, Mississippi

2 On which river does the English city of Derby lie? Derwent, Tamar, Severn

3 Robben Island lies in the bay of which city? Cape Town, Sydney, Bombay

4 The Bitter Lakes are located in which canal? Panama Canal, Suez Canal, Kiel Canal

5 In the film *Superman II*, Lois Lane fell into which waterfall? Angel Falls, Niagara Falls, Yosemite Falls

6 Which country surrounds the Sea of Marmara? Bulgaria, Turkey, Russia

7 Which river forms a natural boundary between South Africa and Zimbabwe? Orange River, Zaire, Limpopo

8 The Great Barrier Reef lies off the coast of which Australian state? Western Australia, Tasmania, Queensland

9 Which US state is home to the Waikiki Beach? California, Hawaii, Rhode Island

10 Which band had a 1983 hit with 'Waterfront'? Wet Wet Wet, Marmalade, Simple Minds

ANSWERS

1. Mississippi 2. Derwent 3. Cape Town 4. Suez Canal 5. Niagara Falls
6. Turkey 7. Limpopo 8. Queensland 9. Hawaii 10. Simple Minds

QUIZ 190

1. In which TV sitcom did David Jason play the role of Granville? *Porridge, Open All Hours, Hark At Barker*

2. How is Hansen's Disease otherwise known? Rabies, Leprosy, Malaria

3. In which century was the composer Johann Sebastian Bach born? 17th, 18th, 19th

4. Which body part is missing from Captain Ahab in the novel *Moby Dick*? Eye, Leg, Ear

5. On which London road is the Cenotaph situated? Bow Street, Whitehall, The Strand

6. How many strings does a ukulele have? 3, 4, 5

7. Which football league club moved their base to Milton Keynes in 2003? Wimbledon, Walsall, Millwall

8. In which American city was the sitcom *Happy Days* set? Seattle, Milwaukee, Denver

9. The jackdaw is a member of which bird family? Finch, Hawk, Crow

10. Which member of the pop group Queen had a solo hit in 1991 with 'Driven By You'? Brian May, Roger Taylor, John Deacon

ANSWERS

1. *Open All Hours* 2. Leprosy 3. 17th 4. Leg 5. Whitehall 6. 4 7. Wimbledon
8. Milwaukee 9. Crow 10. Brian May

QUIZ 191

- -

What word represents the following letters in the
   NATO phonetic alphabet?

1   D   Delta, Doctor, Denmark

2   K   Karate, Kilo, King

3   P   Port, Pelican, Papa

4   O   Oliver, Oscar, Ostrich

5   S   Sierra, Spanish, Statue

6   V   Victor, Valerie, Valetta

7   I   Ivy, India, Israel

8   M   Monsoon, Mike, Maverick

9   Z   Zodiac, Zulu, Zion

10   Q   Queen, Quiz, Quebec

ANSWERS

1. Delta 2. Kilo 3. Papa 4. Oscar 5. Sierra 6. Victor 7. India 8. Mike 9. Zulu
10. Quebec

QUIZ 192

1 What provides the staple diet of the blue whale?
Squid, Seagulls, Krill

2 What nationality is Aladdin? Greek, Persian,
Chinese

3 Which novel features the character of Gabriel
Oak? *Far From The Madding Crowd*, *Little Women*,
Good Wives

4 What year witnessed the death of Winston
Churchill? 1963, 1964, 1965

5 Which American Indian tribe was led by
Geronimo? Apache, Sioux, Blackfoot

6 What flower is shown on the badge of Glamorgan
County Cricket Club? Rose, Daffodil, Lily

7 What part of his body did Vincent Van Gogh cut
off? Left ear, Right thumb, Left thumb

8 What was founded by Henri Jean Dunant in 1864?
The Red Cross, The Jockey Club, The League Of
Nations

9 Who sang the Bond theme for You Only Live
Twice? Lulu, Nancy Sinatra, Shirley Bassey

10 Which capital city stands on the River Potomac?
Washington DC, Ottawa, Canberra

ANSWERS

1. Krill 2. Chinese 3. *Far From The Madding Crowd* 4. 1965 5. Apache
6. Daffodil 7. Left ear 8. The Red Cross 9. Nancy Sinatra 10 Washington DC

QUIZ 193

• •

1. Who played John Brown in the film *Mrs Brown*?
   Billy Connolly, Robbie Coltrane, John Hurt

2. Which character was called Zeke in *The Wizard Of Oz*?   Cowardly Lion, Scarecrow, The Tin Man

3. Who played Sally in *When Harry Met Sally*?
   Melanie Griffith, Sandra Bullock, Meg Ryan

4. Who played Doug Roberts in *Towering Inferno*?
   Steve McQueen, Paul Newman, Robert Wagner

5. Which 1990 film earned Whoopi Goldberg a Best Supporting Actress Oscar?   *Ghost*, *Sister Act*, *The Color Purple*

6. Which pop star links the films *Roadie* and *Union City*?   Tina Turner, Debbie Harry, Whitney Houston

7. Which detective was played by Warner Oland?
   Sherlock Holmes, Father Brown, Charlie Chan

8. For which film did Meryl Streep win her second Best Actress Oscar?   *A Cry In The Dark*, *Silkwood*, *Sophie's Choice*

9. In which film did Clint Eastwood play a gunslinger called William Munny?   *Unforgiven*, *Pale Rider*, *Hang Em High*

10. In a 1984 film, the town of Kingston Falls was invaded by what?   Gremlins, Triffids, Spiders

ANSWERS

1. Billy Connolly 2. Cowardly Lion 3. Meg Ryan 4. Paul Newman 5. *Ghost*
6. Debbie Harry 7. Charlie Chan 8. *Sophie's Choice* 9. Unforgiven
10. Gremlins

QUIZ 194

1 Who presented *The Krypton Factor*?   Angela Rippon, Gordon Burns, Les Dawson

2 In which film did Julia Roberts play the role of Maggie Carpenter?   *Notting Hill*, *Runaway Bride*, *The Mexican*

3 Who managed the England soccer team at the 1986 World Cup finals?   Joe Mercer, Bobby Robson, Howard Wilkinson

4 In which decade did Edgar Allan Poe die?   1640s, 1740s, 1840s

5 From which language does the word alcohol derive?   Arabic, Latin, Spanish

6 Which film featured the Bond girl, Pussy Galore?   *Thunderball*, *Goldfinger*, *Dr No*

7 What animals is the artist George Stubbs known for painting?   Deers, Horses, Dogs

8 Which supermodel is nicknamed The Body?   Naomi Campbell, Rachel Hunter, Elle Macpherson

9 Which fish family does the goldfish belong to?   Carp, Pike, Herring

10 Which novel is sub-titled *Autobiography Of A Horse*?   *Black Beauty*, *National Velvet*, *The Horse Whisperer*

ANSWERS

1. Gordon Burns 2. Runaway Bride 3. Bobby Robson 4. 1840s 5. Arabic
6. *Goldfinger* 7. Horses 8. Elle Macpherson 9. Carp 10. *Black Beauty*

QUIZ 195

- -

1 What does the D stand with regard to the sporting organisation the WDC? Decathlon, Darts, Draughts

2 How many periods comprise an ice hockey match? 3, 4, 6

3 Which US baseball team is known as The Brewers? Cleveland, Milwaukee, Toronto

4 Which country hosted the Winter Olympics of 1932, 1960, 1980 and 2002? Italy, France, USA

5 Which animal completes the name of the St Louis American football team? Eagles, Rams, Bears

6 What were the Commonwealth Games originally called? Friendly Games, Crown Games, Empire Games

7 Which Spanish club won the UEFA Cup in 2004? Barcelona, Valencia, Seville

8 In which sport do competitors "duck the boom"? Pole vault, Yachting, Boxing

9 In which sport did the Wasps win the Heineken Cup in 2004? Polo, Speedway, Rugby union

10 In May 2004, Gerard Houllier waved goodbye to which football club? Liverpool, Millwall, Chelsea

ANSWERS

1. Darts 2. 3 3. Milwaukee 4. USA 5. Rams 6. Empire Games 7. Valencia
8. Yachting 9. Rugby union 10. Liverpool

QUIZ 196

1 What is the capital of Turkey?   Bursa, Ankara, Izmir

2 What colour are the sport questions in the game of Trivial Pursuit?   Orange, Red, Blue

3 Where is the Mound of Mars Positive found? Venus, The brain, Palm of the hand

4 What is the chief ingredient of risotto?   Noodles, Curry, Rice

5 In a church what is kept in a stoup?   Holy water, Prayer books, Incense

6 The Pied Piper drowned the rats of Hamelin in which river?   Danube, Weser, Elbe

7 Who wrote the play *Cat On A Hot Tin Roof*?   Paul Simon, Tennessee Williams, George Bernard Shaw

8 What was the title of the song that won the Eurovision Song Contest in 2004?   'Wild Chants', 'Wild Women', 'Wild Dances'

9 What is the closest capital city to the equator? Mexico City, Quito, Cairo

10 What colour are budgies in the wild?   Green, Blue, Yellow

ANSWERS

1. Ankara 2. Orange 3. Palm of the hand 4. Rice 5. Holy water 6. Weser
7. Tennessee Williams 8. 'Wild Dances' 9. Quito 10. Green

QUIZ 197

1 To what race of people does Lieutenant Worf belong in *Star Trek: The Next Generation*? Vulcan, Klingon, Romulan

2 What is Radar O'Reilly's rank in *M*A*S*H*? Colonel, Captain, Corporal

3 Who pilots Thunderbird 3 in *Thunderbirds*? Scott, Virgil, Alan

4 In 1991, Amos Brearley retired as the landlord of which TV public house? The Rovers Return, The Woolpack, The Nags Head

5 How were Bodie, Doyle and Cowley known on TV? *The Protectors*, *The A Team*, *The Professionals*

6 On whose novel was the TV series *Blott On The Landscape* based? HE Bates, Tom Sharpe, Austen

7 David Sneddon was the first to win which reality TV show? Pop Idol, Fame Academy, Survivor

8 What is the name of Tony and Carmela's daughter in The Sopranos? Lea, Meadow, Summer

9 The pilot episode of which TV series was entitled *Prisoner And Escort*? *Bad Girls*, *Porridge*, *Birds Of A Feather*

10 Which TV hero worked for the OSI? Michael Knight, Joe 90, Six Million Dollar Man

ANSWERS

QUIZ 198

• •

1 Where on the body is a dolly varden worn?
   Around the waist, On the feet, On the head

2 Which singer played Don Johnson's wife in *Miami Vice*? Sheena Easton, Carly Simon, Patti Smith

3 What was the name of the backing band of the rock star Joe Cocker? The Sound Of Music, My Fair Ladies, The Grease Band

4 In which TV show spin-off from *Friends* does Matt Le Blanc play the title role? Ross, Chandler, Joey

5 Who succeeded Winston Churchill as Prime Minister in 1955? Harold Macmillan, Anthony Eden, Clement Atlee

6 What name is given to a birds second stomach?
   Gizzard, Grinder, Gusset

7 Who played Velvet in the film *National Velvet*?
   Joan Collins, Vivien Leigh, Elizabeth Taylor

8 Who won a Best Director Oscar for A Beautiful Mind? Sam Mendes, Tony Scott, Ron Howard

9 What did Shylock demand a pound of in the Shakespeare play *The Merchant Of Venice*? Gold, Sausages, Flesh

10 After whom is the airport in Venice named?
   Marco Polo, Antonio Vivaldi, Michelangelo

ANSWERS

QUIZ 199

• •

Where were the following famous people born?

1 Linford Christie   Barbados, Jamaica, Wales
2 Gloria Estefan   Cuba, Peru, Nicaragua
3 Rudyard Kipling   India, Australia, Canada
4 Freddie Mercury   Kenya, Zanzibar, Malaysia
5 Napoleon Bonaparte   Sicily, Corsica, Elba
6 Irving Berlin   Germany, USA, Russia
7 The Bee Gees   Isle of Man, Australia, Scotland
8 Robert Maxwell   Poland, Hungary, Czechoslovakia
9 Prince Philip   Zante, Rhodes, Corfu
10 JRR Tolkien   Argentina, South Africa, France

ANSWERS

1. Jamaica 2. Cuba 3. India 4. Zanzibar 5. Corsica 6. Russia 7. Isle of Man
8. Czechoslovakia 9. Corfu 10. South Africa

QUIZ 200

• •

1 Which Australian city contains the most skyscrapers? Brisbane, Canberra, Melbourne

2 In an Aesop fable what animal lost a race to a tortoise? Greyhound, Hare, Cheetah

3 Where was the martial arts star Jackie Chan born? Taiwan, USA, Hong Kong

4 What animal does the adjective simian refer to? Whale, Parrot, Ape, Sheep

5 Which author published *Sketches By Boz* in 1836? Emily Bronte, Charles Dickens, Victor Hugo

6 In *Thunderbirds* what is the name of Lady Penelope's chauffeur? Watson, Parker, Jeeves

7 What does the musical instruction Da Capo signify? Gradually louder, Gradually softer, From the beginning

8 Under what name did Rita Crudgington perform in the Eurovision Song Contest? Cheryl Baker, Katrina, Sandie Shaw

9 Who composed the opera Madame Butterfly? Bizet, Verdi, Puccini

10 Who penned an autobiography entitled Reminder? George Cole, Dennis Waterman, Chris Tarrant

ANSWERS

1. Melbourne 2. Hare 3. Hong Kong 4. Ape 5. Charles Dickens 6. Parker
7. From the beginning 8. Cheryl Baker 9. Puccini 10. Dennis Waterman

QUIZ 201

• •

Identify the chemical elements from their symbols

1 K Krypton, Bromine, Potassium

2 N Nitrogen, Neon, Nobelium

3 Cu Copper, Chromium, Cerium

4 Sn Silicon, Strontium, Tin

5 Pb Barium, Lead, Radium

6 Au Argon, Gold, Chlorine

7 S Silver, Sulphur, Steel

8 I Iron, Iridium, Iodine

9 W Tungsten, Uranium, Helium

10 Na Zirconium, Hydrogen, Sodium

ANSWERS

1. Potassium 2. Nitrogen 3. Copper 4. Tin 5. Lead 6. Gold 7. Sulphur
8. Iodine 9. Tungsten 10. Sodium

QUIZ 202

1 What type of leaves provide the staple diet of a silkworm?   Fig, Mulberry, Maple

2 Which song did the New Seekers sing in the Eurovision Song Contest?   'Beg, Steal Or Borrow', 'All Kinds Of Everything', 'Power To All Our Friends'

3 On what day of the week are General Elections traditionally held in Britain?   Tuesday, Thursday, Friday,

4 From which country do the football team Grampus 8 hail?   Brazil, Japan, Belgium

5 Which disciple of Jesus was a tax collector?   Andrew, James, Matthew

6 How is the medical condition epistaxis better known?   Earache, Nose bleed, Cramp

7 Who was the first Beatle to become a grandad?   Ringo Starr, John Lennon, George Harrison

8 Princess Aurora, is the lead character in which ballet?   *Swan Lake*, *The Firebird*, *Sleeping Beauty*

9 In which decade did Barbie dolls first go on sale?   1940s, 1950s, 1960s

10 What is a gross minus a score of?   124, 104, 84

ANSWERS

1. Mulberry 2. 'Beg, Steal or Borrow' 3. Thursday 4. Japan 5. Matthew
6. Nose bleed 7. Ringo Starr 8. *Sleeping Beauty* 9 1950s 10. 124

QUIZ 203

• •

1 In which country is the Dolomites mountain range located? Belgium, Italy, Austria

2 What name are given to counties in Switzerland? Duchys, Cantons, Castes

3 Which European country's parliament is called The Storting? Andorra, Norway, Sweden

4 What is the second most highly populated city in Spain? Valencia, Malaga, Barcelona

5 In which country does the River Danube reach the sea? Romania, Hungary, Germany

6 Which city is known as The Daughter of the Baltic? Moscow, Helsinki, Copenhagen

7 The Mazurka is the national dance of which country? Latvia, Poland, Estonia

8 What is Italy's busiest port? Genoa, Bari, Cagliari

9 Which European city was the final destination of the double decker bus, in the 1962 film *Summer Holiday*? Naples, Rome, Athens

10 Domingo is the Spanish for what day of the week? Sunday, Tuesday, Saturday

ANSWERS

1. Italy 2. Cantons 3. Norway 4. Barcelona 5. Romania 6. Helsinki 7. Poland
8. Genoa 9. Athens 10. Sunday

QUIZ 204

• •

1 What name is given to a male swan?   Cob, Hob, Nob

2 In which capital city is the opera Tosca set?   Paris, Vienna, Rome

3 Which song has been a hit for Simon & Garfunkel and The Bangles?   'Cecilia', 'Hazy Shade Of Winter', 'The Sound of Silence'

4 In which city was Anwar Sadat assassinated in 1981?   Tel Aviv, Cairo, Jerusalem

5 What does the E stand for in the name of E Nesbit, the author of The Railway Children?   Emily, Edith, Eileen

6 What house is Harry Potter in at Hogwarts?   Slytherin, Gryffindor, Ravenclaw

7 Which Hollywood star voiced Sinbad in the 2003 animation, *Sinbad: Legend Of The Seven Seas*?   Matt Damon, Brad Pitt, Ed Norton

8 Which US city is known as The Athens of America?   Seattle, Boston, Anchorage

9 What name is given to a male mermaid?   Merpage, Merman, Mermale

10 Which singer was born Natalie McIntyre?   Macy Gray, Nina Simone, Natalie Cole

ANSWERS

1. Cob 2. Rome 3. 'Hazy Shade Of Winter' 4. Cairo 5. Edith 6. Gryffindor
7. Brad Pitt 8. Boston 9. Merman 10. Macy Gray

QUIZ 205

• •

1 What colour are the history questions in the game of Trivial Pursuit?   Pink, Yellow, Brown

2 What colour are the spots on the jersey worn by the King of the Mountain in the Tour de France? White, Gold, Red

3 Which pop group had hits with the songs, 'Banner Man' and 'Melting Pot'?   Blue Oyster Cult, Blue Mink, Climax Blues Band

4 In heraldry what colour is sable?   Black, Purple, Scarlet

5 What is the nickname of US state, Kentucky?   The Bluegrass State, Orange County, Green Belt State

6 What colour are the benches in the House of Commons?   Brown, Green, Amber

7 Other than white, what colour features on the Vatican flag?   Pink, Violet, Yellow

8 In which film did Brooke Shields find herself marooned on a desert island? *The Green Mile*, *Black Rain*, *The Blue Lagoon*

9 What colour is the zero compartment on a roulette wheel?   Red, Green, White

10 What colour are the shirts worn by New Zealands rugby union team?   Gold, Black, Crimson

ANSWERS

1. Yellow 2. Red 3. Blue Mink 4. Black 5. The Bluegrass State 6. Green
7. Yellow 8. The Blue Lagoon 9. Green 10. Black

QUIZ 206

. . . .

1 In what decade did Emily Bronte die?   1820s, 1840s, 1860s

2 How many signs of the zodiac are represented by horned animals?   3, 4, 5

3 Which novel was a sequel to *Kidnapped*? *Rebecca*, *Emma*, *Catriona*

4 What colour wedding dress is traditionally worn by a Chinese bride?   Black, Maroon, Red

5 In which country is the sitcom *Allo Allo* set? Germany, France, Wales

6 Which Australian city is overlooked by the Blue Mountains?   Sydney, Canberra, Melbourne

7 What was Doc Holliday's occupation?   Barber, Dentist, Vet

8 How many pieces are on a backgammon board at the start of play?   10, 30, 100

9 In which film did Robin Williams and Joan Cusack play brother and sister?   *The Fisher King*, *Toys*, *Jumanji*

10 What does the L stand for with regard to the camera abbreviation SLR?   Lens, Long, Lock

ANSWERS

1. 1840s 2. 3 3. *Catriona* 4. Red 5. France 6. Sydney 7. Dentist 8. 30 9. Toys 10. Lens (Single Lens Reflex)

QUIZ 207

1 Which football club play their home matches at Tannadice Park?   Hearts, Dundee Utd, Aberdeen

2 What is the nickname of Darlington FC?   The Quakers, The Imps, The Saints

3 Which football club moved to the New Den? Manchester City, Millwall, Mansfield

4 Which club did Martin O'Neil leave to manage Celtic?   Southampton, Leicester City, Arsenal

5 With which club did Stanley Matthews end his playing career?   Blackpool, Bolton Wanderers, Stoke City

6 Which city witnessed the Heysel Stadium tragedy in 1985?   Brussels, Lisbon, Paris

7 For which club did Wayne Rooney make his debut?   Liverpool, Everton, Fulham

8 Which club was originally called Pine Villa?   Aston Villa, Oldham Athletic, Norwich City

9 In what decade was the European Footballer Of The Year Award first presented?   1940s, 1950s, 1960s

10 What nationality is the football star Johann Cruyff? French, German, Dutch

ANSWERS

1. Dundee Utd 2. The Quakers 3. Millwall 4. Leicester City 5. Stoke City
6. Brussels 7. Everton 8. Oldham Athletic 9. 1950s 10. Dutch

QUIZ 208

• •

1 Which novel introduced readers to the character of Captain Nemo? *War Of The Worlds*, *20,000 Leagues Under The Sea*, *The Time Machine*

2 Who founded the Frosted Food Company in 1924? Dr Pepper, Clarence Birdseye, Frank Findus

3 In what decade did nylon first go on sale to the public? 1920s, 1930s, 1950s

4 Which monarch claimed that she took a bath at least once a month, "whether she needed it or no"? Queen Victoria, Elizabeth I, Marie Antoinette

5 A Raytheone Raydarange was an early prototype of what? Television, Computer, Microwave oven

6 Who sang the theme song for Dad's Army? Bud Flanagan, Chesney Allen, Norman Wisdom

7 In which US stare did McDonalds open its first fast food retail outlet in 1948? Texas, Iowa, California

8 What is the worlds second highest mountain? Mount Kenya, K2, Kangchenjunga

9 Who composed the Planets Suite? Dvorak, Holst, Elgar

10 How much does the London property of Mayfair cost to purchase in Monopoly? £400, £300, £500

ANSWERS

1. *20,000 Leagues Under The Sea* 2. Clarence Birdseye 3. 1930s
4. Elizabeth I 5. Microwave oven 6. Bud Flanagan 7. California 8. K2
9. Holst 10. £400

QUIZ 209

• •

Identify the TV soaps from each trio of characters

1 Susan Kennedy, Lyn Scully, Ben Kirk   *The Sullivans, Neighbours, The Flying Doctors*

2 Stephanie Rogers, Katherine Wentworth, Donna Krebbs   *Baywatch, Dallas, Beverly Hills 90210*

3 PC Bellamy, Sergeant Merton, PC Bradley   *Juliet Bravo, Heartbeat, Soldier Soldier*

4 Staff Nurse Hill, Nurse Megan Roach, Dr Kaminski   *Casualty, ER, Dr Kildare*

5 Candice Stowe, Blanche Hunt, Karen McDonald   *Hollyoaks, Peyton Place, Coronation Street*

6 Matthew Blaisdee, Cecil Colby, Mark Jennings   *As The World Turns, Dynasty, Flamingo Road*

7 Barbara Hunter, Nicola Freeman, Jill Chance   *Emergency Ward 10, Crossroads, Night & Day*

8 Mo Harris, Lucy Beale, Asif Malik   *Brookside, EastEnders, Family Affairs*

9 Natalie Buxton, Sylvia Hollamby, Tina Purvis   *Prisoner Cell Block H, Bad Girls, Footballer's Wives*

10 Frankie Smith, Chris Tate, Laurel Potts   *The Newcomers, The Archers, Emmerdale*

ANSWERS

1. *Neighbours* 2. *Dallas* 3. *Heartbeat* 4. *Casualty* 5. *Coronation Street*
6. *Dynasty* 7. *Crossroads* 8. *EastEnders* 9. *Bad Girls* 10. *Emmerdale*

QUIZ 210

....

1 In what decade did wrapped sliced bread first go on sale in Britain?   1930s, 1960s, 1890s

2 Tobruk, scene of heavy fighting in World War II, is in which country?   Morocco, France, Libya

3 What did my true love give to me on the 12th day of Christmas?   Maids, Drummers, Pipers

4 Which nation's bank inaugurated the Nobel Prize for Economics in 1969?   Norway, Finland, Sweden

5 Who was the first man to cross Niagara Falls on a tightrope?   Charles Blondin, Matthew Webb, Henry Stanley

6 In which TV series did Dirk Benedict play Lieutenant Starbuck?   *Battlestar Galactica*, *SWAT*, *Buck Rogers In The 25th Century*

7 In which song did Michael Jackson sing the line, "Just remember to always think twice"?   'Bad', 'Beat It', 'Billie Jean'

8 In which film did Fred Astaire sing Cheek To Cheek?   *Shall We Dance*, *Top Hat*, *Easter Parade*

9 Who created *Star Trek*?   Terry Nation, Gene Roddenberry, Douglas Adams

10 Which comedian was born Chris Collins? Graham Norton, Frank Skinner, Ben Elton

ANSWERS

1. 1930s 2. Libya 3. Drummers 4. Bank of Sweden 5. Charles Blondin
6. *Battlestar Galactica* 7. 'Billie Jean' 8. Top Hat 9. Gene Roddenberry
10. Frank Skinner

QUIZ 211

- -

1 In the world of transport what is a TGV?
   Hovercraft, Train, Helicopter

2 Which shipping company did the Titanic belong
   to?   Green Flag, White Star, Red Arrow

3 Which famed road runs from Chicago to Los
   Angeles?   Route 66, Route 88, Route 99

4 LB is the international car registration plate for
   which country? Liberia, Libya, Lebanon

5 What was the name of the first steamship to cross
   the Atlantic Ocean?   Challenger, Savannah, Great
   Eastern

6 Which car manufacturer has made models called
   the Fox and the Passat?   Ford, Saab, Volkswagen

7 Which US city is served by Stapleton Airport?
   Washington DC, San Jose, Denver

8 What year witnessed the sinking of the Herald of
   Free Enterprise ferry?   1987, 1989, 1991

9 P is the international car registration plate of
   which country?   Poland, Portugal, Peru

10 Which car manufacturer has made models called
    the Quest and the Patrol?   Fiat, Nissan, Datsun

ANSWERS

1. Train 2. White Star 3. Route 66 4. Liberia 5. Savannah 6. Volkswagen
7. Denver 8. 1987 9. Portugal 10. Nissan

QUIZ 212

. . . .

1 What type of creature is a taipan? Parrot, Tiger, Snake

2 In what decade did the Open University award its first degrees in the UK? 1980s, 1970s, 1960s

3 Ilium was the Latin name for which ancient city? Sparta, Troy, Olympia

4 In which country is the headquarters of the Nestle confectionary company? USA, Switzerland, Japan

5 What is the former name of Bolivia? Upper Amazon, Upper Peru, Upper Argentina

6 Which British city has the most canals? London, Birmingham, Leeds

7 What is the nationality of the singer Van Morrison? Irish, Welsh, Scottish

8 Which of the world's continents contains the most countries? Asia, Europe, Africa

9 Which of the Teletubbies sports a triangular antenna? La La, Tinky Winky, Dipsy

10 What colour is the Victoria Line on a London underground map? Brown, Blue, Black

ANSWERS

1. Snake 2. 1970s 3. Troy 4. Switzerland 5. Upper Peru 6. Birmingham
7. Irish 8. Africa 9. Tinky Winky 10. Blue

QUIZ 213

• •

Who penned the following autobiographies?

1 The Other Side Of The Street   Martha Reeves,
   Jean Alexander, Michael Douglas

2 The Greatest Game Of All   Jack Nicklaus, Bobby
   Charlton, Pete Sampras

3 Just Williams   Robin Williams, Venus Williams,
   Kenneth Williams

4 Coal Miner's Daughter   Dolly Parton, Loretta Lynn,
   Tammy Wynette

5 My Name Escapes Me   Ronnie Biggs, Alec
   Guinness, Bill Clinton

6 The Full Monty   Robert Carlyle, Lord Mountbatten,
   Jim Davidson

7 Moonwalk   Sting, Neil Armstrong, Michael
   Jackson

8 Being Myself   Michael Barrymore, Billie Jean King,
   Martina Navratilova

9 Where's Harry   Harold Wilson, Harry Houdini,
   Harry Carpenter

10 Arias And Raspberries   Peter Sellers, Spike
    Milligan, Harry Secombe

ANSWERS

QUIZ 214

. . . .

1 Which saints cross does not appear on the Union Jack? Andrew, David, Patrick

2 Who was the first cricketer to score 10,000 test runs? David Gower, Sunil Gavaskar, Geoff Boycott

3 What is the most southerly point of mainland England called? Snake Point, Lizard Point, Toad Point

4 Which detective lived on Punchbowl Hill? Sexton Blake, Lord Peter Wimsey, Charlie Chan

5 Who penned the autobiography Jack Of All Trades? Jack Nicholson, Jack Warner, Jack Wilde

6 In Spain, what is sold in a shop called a bodega? Fruit, Wine, Meat

7 What was Elizabeth Taylor's profession in the film *Butterfield* Prostitute, Beautician, Singer

8 What is the name of the central family in the comedy series *Some Mothers Do Ave' Em*? Turner, Clayton, Spencer

9 What marine creature is often accompanied by pilot fish? Whale, Squid, Shark

10 Which country and western star had a hit with 'A Boy Named Sue'? Johnny Cash, Jim Reeves, Kenny Rogers

ANSWERS

1. David 2. Sunil Gavaskar 3. Lizard Point 4. Charlie Chan 5. Jack Warner
6. Wine 7. Prostitute 8. Spencer 9. Shark 10. Johnny Cash

QUIZ 215

- -

1 What part of Adam's body was used to make Eve?
   Rib, Thumb, Toe

2 On which peak did Moses receive the Ten
   Commandments? Mount Olympus, Mount Sinai,
   Mount Ararat

3 Who replaced Judas as one of the twelve
   apostles? Paul, Matthias, John

4 Which book of the Bible recounted the story of
   the Great Flood? Genesis, Kings, Exodus

5 Who travelled to Nineveh after being swallowed
   by a whale? Samuel, Jonah, Lazarus

6 Which book of the Bible chronicles the
   destruction of the walls of Jericho? Chronicles,
   Ruth, Joshua

7 Which biblical character killed one thousand
   Philistines? Samson, Herod, Lot

8 To which land did Cain flee after killing Abel? Lot,
   Sodom, Gethsemane

9 Who was thrown into the lion's den by King
   Darius? Ahab, Daniel, Salome

10 Who succeeded Moses as the leader of the
   Israelites? Abraham, Isaac, Joshua

ANSWERS

1. Rib 2. Mount Sinai 3. Matthias 4. Genesis 5. Jonah 6. Joshua 7. Samson
8. Lot 9. Daniel 10. Joshua

QUIZ 216

- -

1 Where is the caudal fin on the body of a fish?
   Back, Side, Tail

2 Which character was portrayed by Mike McShane
   in the film, *Robin Hood Prince Of Thieves*? Friar
   Tuck, Robin Hood, Little John

3 Which 20th century war witnessed Operation
   Desert Storm? The Gulf War, World War II, The
   Korean War

4 What is the more common name for the Aurora
   Australis? Southern Lights, Bailey's Beads,
   Northern Lights

5 Brazil and Washington are both varieties of which
   fruit? Plum, Pineapple, Strawberry

6 In what year did London's first airport open?
   1909, 1919, 1929

7 How many lines comprise a limerick? 5, 7, 9

8 In which country did chutney originate? China,
   USA, India

9 In the Bible what was known as, the Staff of Life?
   Wine, Fish, Bread

10 Where was the Royal Mint located prior to 1810?
   Tower of London, Edinburgh Castle, Balmoral

ANSWERS

1. Tail 2. Friar Tuck 3. The Gulf War 4. Southern Lights 5. Plum 6. 1919
7. 5 8. India 9. Bread 10. Tower of London

QUIZ 217

• •

1 After how many years is a quadricennial celebrated?   4000, 400, 40

2 How many Oscars did the film *Schindler's List* win?   3, 7, 9

3 How many years of marriage are celebrated in an Emerald Anniversary?   45, 55, 65

4 How many white squares are there on a chess board?   28, 34, 32

5 How many crochets are there in a semi-breve?   2, 4, 8

6 By 2000 how many Popes had been called John?   13, 23, 53

7 How many legs does a starfish have?   5, 7, 12

8 How many degrees are in a circle?   120, 180, 360

9 How many points did Jemini record in the 2003 Eurovision Song Contest?   None, 1, 50

10 How many pawns does each player have at the start of a game of chess?   6, 8, 10

ANSWERS

1. 400 2. 7 3. 55 4. 32 5. 4 6. 23 7. 5 8. 360 9. None 10. 8

QUIZ 218

. . . .

1 What is the middle name of Jimmy Carter?
   Prince, Duke, Earl

2 Where in the body is the metatarsal arch?   Ear,
   Foot, Armpit

3 What colour is the property of Picadilly on a
   Monopoly board?   Red, Yellow, Blue

4 Which London club won the FA Cup in 1975?
   Chelsea, Charlton Athletic, West Ham Utd, Fulham

5 Which woman won the most Grammy Awards in
   the 20th century?   Aretha Franklin, Madonna,
   Britney Spears

6 Which musical features the song 'Don't Rain On
   My Parade'?   *Singin' In The Rain*, *Gigi*, *Funny Girl*

7 Which Biblical story was the subject of a painting
   by Leonardo da Vinci?   The Crucifixion of Christ,
   The Feeding Of The 5000, The Last Supper

8 To which actress did Humphrey Bogart say,
   "Here's looking at you kid"?   Celia Johnson, Bette
   Davis, Ingrid Bergman

9 Which instrument is associated with the literary
   character, Captain Corelli?   Cornet, Flute, Mandolin

10 What is the name of the US central bank?   Bank
   of Congress, Federal Reserve System, Fort Knox

ANSWERS

1. Earl 2. Foot 3. Yellow 4. West Ham Utd 5. Aretha Franklin 6. *Funny Girl*
7. The Last Supper 8. Ingrid Bergman 9. Mandolin 10. Federal Reserve
System

QUIZ 219

1 Which capital city lies on the island of Honshu? Suva, Tokyo, Jakarta

2 From which country did East Timor gain independence? Indonesia, Malaysia, Taiwan

3 Kandahar and Herat are two major cities in which country? Bangladesh, Afganistan, Borneo

4 The game of snooker originated in which country? India, Thailand, Pakistan

5 What does the word sayonara mean in the Japanese language? Hello, Goodbye, I love you

6 On which river is the Tarbela Dam? Indus, Ganges, Mekong

7 What is the former name of Ho Chi Minh City? Peking, Formosa, Saigon

8 What is the official language of China? Malay, Canton, Mandarin

9 Ikebana is the Japanese art of what? Paper folding, Flower arranging, Self defence

10 What became an autonomous region of China in 1965? Hong Kong, Tibet, Macau

ANSWERS

1. Tokyo 2. Indonesia 3. Afganistan 4. India 5. Goodbye 6. Indus 7. Saigon
8. Mandarin 9. Flower arranging 10. Tibet

QUIZ 220

• •

1 Susan Brown was the first woman to compete in which sporting event? The Grand National, Tour de France, University Boat Race

2 What is the most southerly state of the USA? South Dakota, Texas, Hawaii

3 Who had a 2001 hit with a cover version of the song 'Uptown Girl'? Blue, Westlife, So Solid Crew

4 What is the hobby of Norman Bates in the film *Psycho*? Origami, Butterfly collecting, Taxidermy

5 What was the name of Roy Rogers dog? Bullet, Trigger, Duke

6 What is the American football equivalent of a full back in soccer? Safety, Hooker, Backliner

7 In the rhyme Who Killed Cock Robin, who made Cock Robin's shroud? Fly, Beetle, Sparrow

8 Who does Cyrano de Bergerac fall in love with? Roxanne, Rapunzel, Rosebud

9 Who won a Best Supporting Actor Oscar for his role in the film, *Jerry Maguire*? Tom Cruise, Jude Law, Cuba Gooding Jnr

10 In Dad's Army, what is the oldest member of the squad's surname? Wilson, Godfrey, Walker

ANSWERS

1. University Boat Race 2. Hawaii 3. Westlife 4. Taxidermy 5. Bullet 6. Safety
7. Beetle 8. Roxanne 9. Cuba Gooding Jnr 10. Godfrey

QUIZ 221

. . . .

1 Who wrote the lyrics for the musical *Starlight Express*? Ben Elton, Richard Stilgoe, Tim Rice

2 Which film musical opens with The Deadwood Stage? *Oklahoma*, *Calamity Jane*, *Carousel*

3 On whose novel was the musical *Half A Sixpence* based? Charles Dickens, HG Wells, Walter Scott

4 What national flower is the subject of a song in *The Sound Of Music*? Tulip, Lotus, Edelweiss

5 Which stage musical features Baggy Trousers and Shut Up? *Mama Mia*, *Our House*, *Grease*

6 In which film did Hazel O'Connor play a punk band lead singer? *Quadrophenia*, *The Great Rock And Roll Swindle*, *Breaking Glass*

7 Which film star directed the 1969 musical *Hello Dolly*? Howard Keel, Gene Kelly, Bing Crosby

8 Who played the role of Satine in the 2001 film *Moulin Rouge*? Renee Zellweger, Queen Latifah, Nicole Kidman

9 In which musical did Twiggy play Polly Browne? *The Boy Friend*, *The Jazz Singer*, *Star*

10 Which musical features the song 'Sit Down You're Rocking The Boat'? *Guys And Dolls*, *Anchors Aweigh*, *Show Boat*

ANSWERS

1. Richard Stilgoe 2. *Calamity Jane* 3. HG Wells 4. Edelweiss 5. *Our House*
6. *Breaking Glass* 7. Gene Kelly 8. Nicole Kidman 9. *The Boy Friend*
10. *Guys And Dolls*

QUIZ 222

1. Who was Chancellor of the Exchequer during the 1926 General Strike in Britain? Winston Churchill, Neville Chamberlain, Stanley Baldwin

2. The Ashburton Treaty set boundaries between which countries? England and Scotland, USA and Canada, Northern Ireland and Republic of Ireland

3. What sport is played by the Phoenix Suns? Baseball, Polo, Basketball

4. Which Monty Python member wrote and performed the theme song for One Foot In The Grave? John Cleese, Terry Gilliam, Eric Idle

5. What is a wobbegong? Hat, Cymbal, Shark

6. Who played Samwise Gangee in *The Lord of the Rings* films? Elijah Wood, Sean Astin, Sean Bean

7. Which musical instrument is Artie Shaw known for playing? Piano, Guitar, Clarinet

8. What material does a currier work with? Leather, Silk, Wool

9. What title is given to Luxembourg's head of state? Prince Regent, Grand Duke, Emperor

10. In what decade was the American football Super Bowl first contested? 1960s, 1940s, 1920s

ANSWERS

1. Winston Churchill 2. USA and Canada 3. Basketball 4. Eric Idle 5. Shark
6. Sean Astin 7. Clarinet 8. Leather 9. Grand Duke 10. 1960s

QUIZ 223

• •

1 A pudu is a small species of what? Horse, Deer, Sheep

2 What was Michael Caine battling against in the film *The Swarm*? Bees, Locusts, Ants

3 If a leaf is described as dentate, what is it shaped like? Egg, Bell, Tooth

4 What bird is known as the harbinger of Spring? Bittern, Cuckoo, Swallow

5 Bluefin and Bonita are both species of what? Skate, Tuna, Herring

6 The adjective leporine refers to which animal? Hare, Beaver, Fox

7 What is the world's largest fish? Whale shark, Barracuda, Marlin

8 What species of duck shares its name with the title of a James Bond film? *Goldeneye*, *Thunderball*, *Moonraker*

9 Red, hermit, horseshoe and edible are all species of what? Spider, Crab, Eel

10 What name is given to any animal that carries its young in a pouch? Omnivore, Marsupial, Ruminant

ANSWERS

1. Deer 2. Bees 3. Tooth 4. Cuckoo 5. Tuna 6. Hare 7. Whale shark
8. *Goldeneye* 9. Crab 10. Marsupial

QUIZ 224

1 What item was invented by an inmate of Newgate Prison?   Toothbrush, Comb, Key ring

2 What is an MP doing if applying for the Chiltern 100's?   Voting on a bill, Resigning, Changing parties

3 On what object is a hardy hole found?   Bell, Anchor, Anvil

4 What name is given to the part of a flag that is nearest to the flagpole?   Fly, Haul, Hoist

5 In which 1991 box office flop did Bruce Willis play a cat burglar?   *Hudson Hawk*, *The Last Boy Scout*, *The Fifth Element*

6 Which football club were surprise winners of the FA Cup in 1988?   Wimbledon, Sunderland, Burnley

7 Moth, Mustard and Cobweb are names of what in a Shakespeare play?   Witches, Spiders, Fairies

8 In what building did Miss Marple investigate her first literary murder case?   Library, Cafe, Vicarage

9 What is Victoria Wood's character's name in *Dinnerladies*?   Laura, Brenda, Laverne

10 Which British Olympian won the most Olympic gold medals in the 20th century?   Sebastian Coe, Steve Redgrave, Daley Thompson

ANSWERS

1. Toothbrush 2. Resigning 3. Anvil 4. Hoist 5. *Hudson Hawk*
6. Wimbledon 7. Fairies 8. Vicarage 9. Brenda 10. Steve Redgrave

QUIZ 225

. . . .

1 What is it said you can get for your thoughts?
Trouble, Ideas, Penny

2 According to the saying, what will faith move?
Heaven, Mountains, Mysteries

3 What is said to be the mother of good fortune?
Efficiency, Luck, Diligence

4 According to the saying, what do good fences
make? Good neighbours, Good homes, Good
gardens

5 What is said to be next to godliness? Charity,
Fortitude, Cleanliness

6 What is said to be the root of all evil? Money,
Ambition, Marriage

7 What word completes the saying, They that dance
must pay the …? Pianist, Fiddler, Conductor

8 What is said to be the best teacher? Conscience,
Patience, Experience

9 According to the saying what can one not make
without breaking eggs? Friends, Souffle,
Omelette

10 What is said to breed contempt? Deceit,
Violence, Familiarity

ANSWERS

1. Penny 2. Mountains 3. Diligence 4. Good neighbours 5. Cleanliness
6. Money 7. Fiddler 8. Experience 9. Omelette 10. Familiarity

QUIZ 226

1 Who managed the England football team at Euro 96? Terry Venables, Graham Taylor, Kevin Keegan

2 Where did the little lamb follow Mary to in the nursery rhyme? School, Shops, Disco

3 What is the square root of 64? 4, 8, 128

4 What flower family does garlic belong to? Fuschia, Lily, Geranium

5 In *Coronation Street*, which character enjoyed an on-off love affair with Cilla Brown? Ashley Peacock, Ken Barlow, Les Battersby

6 Who was embroiled in the 1987 Irangate scandal? Colonel West, Colonel East, Colonel North

7 How many hearts does Dr Who have? None, 2, 7

8 Which female sports star was voted BBC Sports Personality of the Year in 1991? Sally Gunnell, Liz McColgan, Alison Fisher

9 What was the last name of the character played by Dennis Waterman in the TV series *Minder*? McKay, McCann, McKenna

10 What number of Thunderbird is in permanent orbit around the Earth? Thunderbird 5, Thunderbird 6, Thunderbird 11

ANSWERS

1. Terry Venables 2. School 3. 8 4. Lily 5. Les Battersby 6. Colonel North
7. 2 8. Liz McColgan 9. McCann 10. Thunderbird 5

QUIZ 227

1 Which country forms a border with Sudan, Libya, Niger and the Central African Republic? Benin, Ghana, Chad

2 What is the largest lake in Africa? Nyasa, Victoria, Taganayika

3 What is the closest African country to Spain? Algeria, Tunisia, Morocco

4 How does the name of Casablanca translate into English? Castle wine, Empty cape, White house

5 What breed of cat was named after the former name of Ethiopia? Persian, Burmese, Abyssinian

6 Africa's first underground railway system was built in which city? Cairo, Nairobi, Cape Town

7 The majority of the Kalahari Desert lies in which country? Botswana, Lesotho, Gambia

8 Which of the following countries does not form a land border with South Africa? Namibia, Zimbabwe, Angola

9 The Victoria Falls separates Zimbabwe from which other country? Senegal, Zaire, Zambia

10 Which pop group had a 1983 hit with the song 'Africa'? Toto, Wizzard, Kansas

ANSWERS

1. Chad 2. Victoria 3. Morocco 4. White house 5. Abyssinian 6. Cairo
7. Botswana 8. Angola 9. Zambia 10. Toto

QUIZ 228

• •

1 Who piloted the aircraft The Spirit of St Louis?
   Amelia Earhart, Charles Lindbergh, Louis Bleriot

2 What nickname was given to the former world
   champion snooker star, Ray Reardon?   The
   Mummy, Frankenstein, Dracula

3 Who wrote *Jigsaw* in 1923 and went on to
   publish over 700 novels?   Agatha Christie, Barbara
   Cartland, Catherine Cookson

4 In which country was Fidel Castro born?   Cuba,
   Mexico, USA

5 What colour is the mythical horse Pegasus?
   Black, Gold, White

6 Which of the following was not a member of the
   Darling children in Peter Pan?   Wendy, Thomas,
   John

7 In which country was the diarist Anne Frank born?
   Netherlands, Germany, Poland

8 Which of the following is not an animal in the
   Chinese calendar?   Duck, Rat, Horse

9 What is the ruling planet of the star sign of
   Taurus?   Mars, Venus, Saturn

10 What name is given to the sediment at the
   bottom of a wine cask?   Sec, Lees, Legs

ANSWERS

1. Charles Lindbergh 2. Dracula 3. Barbara Cartland 4. Cuba 5. White
6. Thomas 7. Germany 8. Duck 9. Venus 10. Lees

QUIZ 229

1. Which football club finished second in the 2003/04 season? Chelsea, Liverpool, Aston Villa

2. What was voted Best Soap at the 2004 British Soap Awards? *Bad Girls*, *EastEnders*, *Emmerdale*

3. In 2004, who was Lord High Admiral in the UK? Prince Philip, Queen Elizabeth II, Tony Blair

4. How many new countries joined the European Union on May 1, 2004? 1, 5, 10

5. Which *Harry Potter* film was released in 2004? *The Chamber of Secrets*, *The Order Of The Phoenix*, *The Prisoner of Azkaban*

6. Which country hosted the 2004 Eurovision Song Contest? Turkey, France, Belgium

7. Which footballer was the subject of an exhibition at the National Portrait Gallery in London? Michael Owen, David Beckham, Thierry Henry

8. In May 2004, Piers Morgan resigned as editor of which newspaper? *Daily Mirror*, *Sun*, *Daily Mail*

9. Who was voted Best Actor at the 2004 British Soap Awards? Lee Hunter, Shane Richie, David Neilson

10. Which *Thelma and Louise* star had twins in 2004? Geena Davis, Brad Pitt, Susan Sarandon

ANSWERS

1. Chelsea 2. *EastEnders* 3. Queen Elizabeth II 4. 10 5. *The Prisoner of Azkaban* 6. Turkey 7. David Beckham 8. *Daily Mirror* 9. Shane Richie 10. Geena Davis

QUIZ 230

1 Which planet shares its name with the Roman god of the sea? Mars, Neptune, Saturn

2 From which country do the football club Celta Vigo hail? Portugal, Spain, Uruguay

3 Which sugar occurs naturally in milk? Glucose, Bigtose, Lactose

4 With which record company did George Michael begin a court dispute in 1996? Sony, Virgin, RCA

5 What alcoholic drink did the author Laurie Lee enjoy with Rosie? Sherry, Cider, Lager

6 What is the name of the oldest child of Prince Rainier of Monaco? Grace, Albert, Caroline

7 Which pop star shares her name with the former Queen of Carthage? Bjork, Dido, Madonna

8 Who was imprisoned in the Tower of London in 1679, after he was accused of being involved in the Popish Plot? Walter Raleigh, Isaac Newton, Samuel Pepys

9 Which former Wimbledon champion acquired the nickname of Superbrat? John McEnroe, Ilie Nastase, Roscoe Tanner

10 What brass musical instrument is also a bead sewn on to a dress? Trombone, Horn, Bugle

ANSWERS

1. Neptune 2. Spain 3. Lactose 4. Sony 5. Cider 6. Caroline 7. Dido
8. Samuel Pepys 9. John McEnroe 10. Bugle

QUIZ 231

Who is credited with the following quotes?

1 "There can be no whitewash at the White House "
   George Bush Jnr, Richard Nixon, Bill Clinton

2 "Put your trust in God but keep your powder dry "
   Oliver Cromwell, Guy Fawkes, Horatio Nelson

3 "I'm the king of the world, I am the greatest"
   Muhammed Ali, Pele, Mike Tyson

4 "The ballot is stronger than the bullet" John F
   Kennedy, Abraham Lincoln, Che Guevara

5 "Freedom is never voluntarily given by the
   oppressor" Martin Luther King, Robert Mugabe,
   Nelson Mandela

6 "Will no one rid me of this turbulent priest?"
   Henry II, Henry V, Henry VIII

7 "The lady's not for turning" Queen Elizabeth I,
   Margaret Thatcher, Florence Nightingale

8 "Houston, Tranquility Base here, the Eagle has
   landed" John Glenn, Neil Armstrong, Buzz Aldrin

9 "History is bunk" Henry Ford, Tony Blair, Napolean

10 "I sometimes wonder if two thirds of the world is
   covered in red carpet" Prince Charles, Pope John
   Paul II, Julia Roberts

ANSWERS

1. Richard Nixon 2. Oliver Cromwell 3. Muhammed Ali 4. Abraham Lincoln
5, Martin Luther King 6. Henry II 7. Margaret Thatcher 8. Buzz Aldrin
9. Henry Ford 10. Prince Charles

QUIZ 232

- -

1 Which country and western singer died in a plane crash in 1997?   John Denver, Patsy Cline, Jim Reeves

2 What does the I stand for in the police acronym CID?   Institute, Intelligence, Investigation

3 What is the monetary unit of Canada?   Pound, Franc, Dollar

4 In the *Magic Roundabout*, what does the cow Ermintrude always have in her mouth?   Carrot, Flower, Pencil

5 What is Scotland's oldest football club?   Celtic, Rangers, Queen's Park

6 Which novel features Twala and Gagool?   *Last Of The Mohicans*, *Shogun*, *King Solomon's Mines*

7 In which country was the author Salman Rushdie born?   India, USA, Saudi Arabia

8 During which war was the TV drama *Sharpe* set?   Crimean, Napoleonic, Boer

9 Which 1998 film saw Bruce Willis landing on a rogue asteroid heading for Earth?   *Armageddon*, *Starman*, *The Rock*

10 What is bronze's main element?   Iron, Zinc, Copper

ANSWERS

1. John Denver 2. Investigation 3. Dollar 4. Flower 5. Queen's Park 6. *King Solomon's Mines* 7. India 8. Napoleonic 9. *Armageddon* 10. Copper

QUIZ 233

In which film did …

1 Bill Murray play Dr Venkman? *Lost In Translation, Little Shop Of Horrors, Ghostbusters*

2 Renee Zellweger play Roxie Hart? *Jerry Maguire, Chicago, Cold Mountain*

3 Glenn Close play the Marquise de Merteuil? *Hamlet, Dangerous Liaisons, Mars Attacks*

4 Harvey Keitel play Jack Crawford? *The Piano, Copland, Red Dragon*

5 Michelle Pfeiffer play Susie Diamond? *Batman Returns, Dangerous Minds, The Fabulous Baker Boys*

6 Dustin Hoffman play Jack Crabb? *Little Big Man, Death Of A Salesman, Rain Man*

7 Leonardo Di Caprio play Amsterdam Vallon? *The Beach, The Aviator, Gangs Of New York*

8 Kiefer Sutherland play Doc Scurlock? *The Vanishing, Young Guns, A Few Good Men*

9 Drew Barrymore play Dylan Sanders? *ET, Charlies Angels, The Wedding Singer*

10 George Clooney play Captain Billy Tyne? *Three Kings, The Thin Red Line, The Perfect Storm*

ANSWERS

1. *Ghostbusters* 2. *Chicago* 3. *Dangerous Liaisons* 4. *Red Dragon*
5. *The Fabulous Baker Boys* 6. *Little Big Man* 7. *Gangs Of New York*
8. *Young Guns* 9. *Charlies Angels* 10. *The Perfect Storm*

QUIZ 234

. . . .

1 What is a Cambridge Rival? Strawberry, Pear, Plum

2 Who played the title role in the 2003 film, *The Life Of David Gale*? Kevin Spacey, Matthew Modine, Jeff Bridges

3 What colour is Old Kent Road on a Monopoly board? Blue, Brown, Green

4 Who played Gavin Rumsey in the 70s sitcom *The Cuckoo Waltz* and starred in *The Professionals*? Gordon Jackson, Lewis Collins, Martin Shaw

5 In the USA, how many dollars is a sawbuck worth? One, 10, 20

6 Which country's flag flies over Queen Elizabeth Island? Britain, Canada, New Zealand

7 Which former Neighbour's star collected two Brit Awards in 1999? Holly Valance, Natalie Imbruglia, Kylie Minogue

8 In which area of London, was 70s sitcom *Citizen Smith* set? Tooting, Islington, Peckham

9 What is the name of the flying island in Gulliver's Travels? Ruritania, Laputa, Nowhereland

10 Which football striker was the leading goal scorer at the 1982 World Cup finals? Paulo Rossi, Zico, Mario Kempes

ANSWERS

1. Strawberry 2. Kevin Spacey 3. Brown 4. Lewis Collins 5. 10 6. Canada
7. Natalie Imbruglia 8. Tooting 9. Laputa 10. Paulo Rossi

QUIZ 235

- -

1 What is the first name of the Great Gatsby?
   Gordon, Jack, Jay

2 Which sports brand took its name from a variety
   of South African antelope?   Nike, Reebok, Gola

3 Under what three-letter nickname was pop star
   Alison Moyet formerly known?   Bob, Alf, Dan

4 Which boys first name provided the real surname
   of the comedian Eric Morecambe?   Percival,
   Bartholomew, Wilberforce

5 What is the last name of the author of The
   Prisoner Of Zenda?   Faith, Hope, Justice

6 What was Buddy Holly's real first name?   Andrew,
   Charles, Harold

7 What is the first name of the character played by
   Pauline Quirke in the TV comedy series *Birds Of A
   Feather*?   Dorien, Sharon, Linda

8 What R is the middle name of David Beckham?
   Roy, Rupert, Robert

9 What was the surname of the brothers who
   founded the *Guinness Book Of Records*?
   McDonald, McWhirter, McDougall

10 In *Last Of The Summer Wine*, what is Norah Batty's
   deceased husband called?   Peter, Wally, Brian

ANSWERS

1. Jay 2. Reebok 3. Alf 4. Bartholomew 5. Hope 6. Charles 7. Sharon
8. Robert 9. McWhirter 10. Wally

QUIZ 236

1 Moray and culper are both species of what?
Horse, Fox, Eel

2 In which sport is a series of bouts called a
barrage?   Judo, Fencing, Kendo

3 Who was played by Christopher Plummer in *The
Man Who Would Be King*?   Mark Twain, Rudyard
Kipling, Jules Verne

4 What breed of dog is Nipper, the logo on the
HMV record label?   Fox terrier, Poodle, Labrador

5 What name is given to a male donkey? Jack,
John, Joey

6 In 1862, who organised the world's first package
holiday?   Billy Butlin, Henry Lunn, Thomas Cook

7 What is used to flavour the soft drink cola?   Cola
bread, Cola rice, Cola nuts

8 What nationality was the character played by
Sean Connery in the film *The Hunt For Red
October*?   Russian, German, American

9 What bird does the adjective corvine refer to?
Cuckoo, Crow, Cassowary

10 Who was Prime Minister of Great Britain during
the Falklands War? Ted Heath, Margaret Thatcher,
Harold Wilson

ANSWERS

1. Eel 2. Fencing 3. Rudyard Kipling 4. Fox terrier 5. Jack 6. Thomas Cook
7. Cola nuts 8. Russian 9. Crow 10. Margaret Thatcher

QUIZ 237

• •

1 Which European nation first won soccer's World Cup three times?   Italy, England, France

2 Which soap first appeared on British TV in November 1982?   *EastEnders*, *Brookside*, *Casualty*

3 In 1901, Emil Behring was the first person to win what?   Tour de France, Nobel Prize, Victoria Cross

4 Who was the first British scientist to be knighted? Michael Faraday, Joseph Lister, Isaac Newton

5 Who was the first British Royal to graduate from university?   Princess Anne, Prince Edward, Prince Charles

6 According to the proverb, he was a brave man that first ate a what?   Oyster, Chilli, Onion

7 Who won his first snooker world title in 1981? Alex Higgins, Steve Davis, Stephen Hendry

8 Which was the first city to have two TV stations? Manchester, New York, Toronto

9 Who was the first British driver to record 30 Formula One Grand Prix victories? Nigel Mansell, Damon Hill, Jackie Stewart

10 In what year did Queen Elizabeth II become a tax payer for the first time?   1993, 1991, 1987

ANSWERS

1. Italy 2. *Brookside* 3. Nobel Prize 4. Isaac Newton 5. Prince Charles
6. Oyster 7. Steve Davis 8. New York 9. Nigel Mansell 10. 1993

QUIZ 238

• •

1 Which club side did Alf Ramsey manage prior to taking the England job? Newcastle United, Ipswich Town, Blackburn Rovers

2 What type of animal is a sidewinder? Shark, Crab, Snake

3 Which sport featured in the film *Cool Runnings*? Bobsleigh, Swimming, Ice skating

4 Which building witnessed the coronation of Queen Elizabeth II? Windsor Castle, Winchester Cathedral, Westminster Abbey

5 In which film did Jodie Foster play the role of Clarice Starling? *The Accused*, *Silence Of The Lambs*, *Hannibal*

6 What is the second largest French speaking city in the world? Quebec, Montreal, Marseilles

7 What colour does gin become when angostura bitters are added? Black, Blue, Pink

8 In chess, what piece is moved with the rook in the move known as castling? King, Bishop, Pawn

9 Who penned the autobiography, *I Am The Doctor*? Benjamin Spock, Jon Pertwee, Harrison Ford

10 Which football club won Spain's premier league La Liga in 2004? Barcelona, Valencia, Real Madrid

ANSWERS

1. Ipswich Town 2. Snake 3. Bobsleigh 4. Westminster Abbey 5. *Silence Of The Lambs* 6. Montreal 7. Pink 8. King 9. Jon Pertwee 10. Valencia

QUIZ 239

• •

What word is represented by the following phrases in
   Cockney rhyming slang?

1   Cat and mouse   Grouse, House, Spouse

2   Pen and ink   Stink, Think, Mink

3   Mince pies   Flies, Lies, Eyes

4   Bucket and pail   Jail, Sail, Whale

5   Iron tank   Bank, Spank, Rank

6   Rosy Lea   Flea, Tea, Fee

7   Conan Doyle   Soil, Oil, Boil

8   Whistle and flute   Suit, Brute, Newt

9   Noah's ark   Shark, Park, Bark

10   Apple and pears   Bears, Stairs, Fun fairs

ANSWERS

QUIZ 240

1. Which novel features the school bully Flashman? *Great Expectations*, *Tom Brown's Schooldays*, *School For Scandal*

2. What is the highest rank of British peerage? Duke, Marquis, Viscount

3. Which golfer's motto is "Grip it and rip it"? John Daly, Tiger Woods, Nick Faldo

4. After China and India, which country has the third highest population? Nigeria, USA, Russia

5. What type of insect is a katydid? Bee, Stick insect, Grasshopper

6. In what decade did speed cameras first appear on British roads? 1970s, 1980s, 1990s

7. Which company was first called the California Perfume Company? Avon, Chanel, Calvin Klein

8. Which British king's coronation was in 1902? Edward VII, Edward VIII, George V

9. Who was the first US President to hold a patent for an invention? Abraham Lincoln, Thomas Jefferson, Jimmy Carter

10. July 2003 witnessed a fire at the top of which famous tower? Eiffel Tower, Blackpool Tower, Tower of London

ANSWERS

1. *Tom Brown's Schooldays* 2. Duke 3. John Daly 4. USA 5. Grasshopper
6. 1990s 7. Avon 8. Edward VII 9. Abraham Lincoln 10. Eiffel Tower

QUIZ 241

1 The flag of Bolivia depicts six what?   Rifles, Birds, Spears

2 What type of leaf features on the flag of Canada? Oak, Maple, Fig

3 What animal is depicted on the flag of the Falkland Islands?   Sheep, Penguin, Dove

4 What is depicted at the centre of the flag of Cambodia?   Unicorn, Temple, Flower

5 Which of the following colours does not feature on the flag of Hungary?   Blue, Red, White

6 What is depicted in the left hand corner of the flag of Liechtenstein?   Wheel, Rose, Crown

7 How many legs feature on the flag of the Isle Of Man?   2, 3, 4

8 What colour is the eagle on the flag of Albania? Gold, Black, Green

9 Which island country incorporates the George Cross into its flag?   Crete, Malta, Cyprus

10 What tree features on the flag of Lebanon?   Palm, Cedar, Sycamore

ANSWERS

1. Spears 2. Maple 3. Sheep 4. Temple 5. Blue 6. Crown 7. 3 8. Black
9. Malta 10. Cedar

QUIZ 242

. . . .

1 Which TV series centred around the activities of Sunshine Cabs? *Roger Roger, Taxi, Moonlighting*

2 Which religion was founded by Guru Nanak? Buddhist, Sikh, Moonies

3 Who provides the voice of Queen Lillian in the 2004 animated sequel Shrek 2? Cameron Diaz, Judi Dench, Julie Andrews

4 Which Italian city is home to the Rialto Bridge? Venice, Rome, Milan

5 Who served as Vice-President to Bill Clinton? Al Gore, Dick Cheney, Walter Mondale

6 How many of the 7 dwarfs have beards? 1, 6, 7

7 Who first appeared together in Flying Down To Rio? Fred Astaire and Ginger Rogers, Laurel and Hardy, Dean Martin and Jerry Lewis

8 In which month of the year was Julius Caesar killed? March, June, July

9 Who was the second President of the USA? James Monroe, John Adams, Andrew Jackson

10 In 2003, whose 85th birthday party was attended by Bill Clinton and Robert DeNiro? Ronald Reagan, Kirk Douglas, Nelson Mandela

ANSWERS

1. *Taxi* 2. Sikh 3. Julie Andrews 4. Venice 5. Al Gore 6. 6 7. Fred Astaire and Ginger Rogers 8. March 9. John Adams 10. Nelson Mandela

QUIZ 243

- -

1 From which country did Brazil gain independence in the 1820s? Portugal, Spain, Mexico

2 In which country is the Atacama Desert? Bolivia, Chile, Uruguay

3 What is the longest river in South America? River Plate, Orinoco, Amazon

4 Which South American city represents a letter in the NATO phonetic alphabet? Montevideo, Lima, Caracas

5 Which city is overlooked by Sugar Loaf Mountain? Rio de Janeiro, Sao Paulo, Santiago

6 Which country is home to the Angel Falls? Venezuela, Peru, Guatemala

7 Which 1969 film starring Paul Newman ended in Bolivia? *The Sting, Hud, Butch Cassidy And The Sundance Kid*

8 What is the largest species of cat native to South America? Jaguar, Tiger, Bobcat

9 In South America what is the Aconcagua? The largest desert, The highest mountain, The widest canyon

10 Which was the first South American country to win soccer's World Cup? Brazil, Uruguay, Peru

ANSWERS

1. Portugal 2. Chile 3. Amazon 4. Lima 5. Rio de Janeiro 6. Venezuela
7. *Butch Cassidy And The Sundance Kid* 8. Jaguar 9. The highest mountain
10. Uruguay

QUIZ 244

1 What is the chief language of Afghanistan?
   Pushtu, Pulltu, Tugtu

2 How many states of the USA form a border with
   Alaska? None, 3, 5

3 What was the nationality of the 2003 Formula
   One World Champion?   French, German, Finnish

4 In which continent is the worlds longest river?
   North America, Africa, Europe

5 In Disney's animated version of Robin Hood, what
   type of animal is Maid Marian?   Fox, Deer, Chicken

6 What is the nationality of the snooker star Ken
   Doherty?   Canadian, Irish, Australian

7 What is the medical name for the thigh bone?
   Tibia, Ulna, Femur

8 How many different question categories comprise
   the game of Trivial Pursuit?   4, 6, 8

9 In an Italian restaurant, what are gnocchi?   Spices,
   Mushrooms, Dumplings

10 Who played Mrs Robinson in the 1967 film *The
   Graduate*?   Anne Bancroft, Faye Dunaway, Audrey
   Hepburn

ANSWERS

1. Pushtu 2. None 3. German 4. Africa 5. Fox 6. Irish 7. Femur 8. 6
9. Dumplings 10. Anne Bancroft

QUIZ 245

. . . .

1 What is the only bird that can fly backwards? Macaw, Hummingbird, Toucan

2 Which bird conducted the wedding ceremony of the owl and the pussycat? Turkey, Eagle, Goose

3 Which bird lays the largest egg? Emu, Kiwi, Ostrich

4 Which bird congregates in groups called musters? Kingfisher, Peacock, Falcon

5 Who wrote the novel *Swallows And Amazons*? Arthur Ransome, Jack London, Henry Williamson

6 What is the nickname of Notts County FC? Magpies, Nightingales, Owls

7 What was the first name of the character played by John Wayne in the film *True Grit*? Hawk, Swan, Rooster

8 Which singer had a 1984 hit with the song, 'When Doves Cry'? Madonna, Prince, Nena

9 What nickname was bestowed upon the Olympic ski jumper Eddie Edwards? The Seagull, The Eagle, The Kestrel

10 What C word is the collective noun for hawks and falcons? Clutch, Cast, Covey

ANSWERS

1. Hummingbird 2. Turkey 3. Ostrich 4. Peacock 5. Arthur Ransome
6. Magpies 7. Rooster 8. Prince 9. The Eagle 10. Cast

QUIZ 246

. . . .

1 How many years of marriage are celebrated in a Coral Anniversary?   10, 35, 40

2 Which country is home to the Simpson Desert? Australia, Mexico, South Africa

3 What is the traditional colour of New York taxis? White, Yellow, Black

4 Which king founded the Order Of The Garter? Richard III, George III, Edward III

5 In which US state is the Grand Canyon located? Nevada, Arizona, Nebraska

6 Which car manufacturer won five consecutive Formula One world titles between 1999 and 2003?   Williams, Ferrari, McLaren

7 What is the first name of Harrison Ford's character in the *Star Wars* movies?   Han, Ben, Boba

8 What type of hat takes its name from the Spanish for shade?   Beret, Sombrero, Stetson

9 Where in Britain is Cape Wrath?   Scotland, England, Wales

10 Which Shakespeare character is also the name of the second child of David and Victoria Beckham? Othello, Romeo, Oberon

ANSWERS

1. 35 2. Australia 3. Yellow 4. Edward III 5. Arizona 6. Ferrari 7. Han
8. Sombrero 9. Scotland 10. Romeo

QUIZ 247

- -

1 A griffin is half lion, half what?   Man, Eagle, Wolf

2 How was Atlas related to Zeus?   Son, Brother, Nephew

3 On which Greek island did the the minotaur live? Corfu, Lesbos, Crete

4 What special power did the helmet of Perseus give to the wearer?   Invisibility, Flight, ESP

5 Who is the Egyptian god of the sun?   Ta, La, Ra

6 How many eyes does a cyclops have?   1, 10, 100

7 Who was the son of Daedalus? Icarus, Hercules, Oedipus

8 Who killed the Trojan hero Hector?   Helen of Troy, Achilles, Prometheus

9 Which duo founded the city of Rome?   Castor and Pollux, Romulus and Remus, Adam and Eve

10 Who was the Muse of History in Greek mythology?   Uno, Saxo, Clio

ANSWERS

1. Eagle 2. Brother 3. Crete 4, Invisibility 5. Ra 6. 1 7. Icarus 8. Achilles
9. Romulus and Remus 10. Clio

QUIZ 248

1. In which country was Uri Geller born? Greece, Poland, Israel

2. Which novel is narrated by Charles Ryder? *Brideshead Revisited*, *The Eagle Has Landed*, *Lolita*

3. Which Asian city is home to the cricket test match venue, Eden Gardens? Calcutta, Karachi, Bombay

4. Which film marked the directorial debut of Quentin Tarantino? *Pulp Fiction*, *True Romance*, *Reservoir Dogs*

5. What name is given to the compulsive urge to steal? Kleptomania, Meglomania, Pyromania

6. Which of the following does not feature in a string quartet? Cello, Guitar, Viola

7. Which city is home to the Zion Gate and Herod's Gate? Tel Aviv, Jerusalem, Damascus

8. What was the nationality of King Canute? Scottish, Danish, Norwegian

9. Which of the following British cities does not have an underground railway system? Birmingham, London, Glasgow

10. What genre of music is most closely associated with the city of Nashville? Soul, Grunge, Rap, Country & Western

ANSWERS

1. Israel 2. *Brideshead Revisited* 3. Calcutta 4. *Reservoir Dogs*
5. Kleptomania 6. Guitar 7. Jerusalem 8. Danish 9. Birmingham
10. Country & Western

QUIZ 249

1 In The Bangles hit 'Manic Monday', who was sitting next to a crystal blue Italian stream?   Valentino, Napoleon, Mussolini

2 Where does The Beatles' Long And Winding Road lead to?   Your door, Penny Lane, True love

3 What dolls are sung about in 'Livin La Vida Loca'? California dolls, Cabbage Patch dolls, Voodoo dolls

4 Which Abba hit says, "I feel like I win when I lose"? SOS, Waterloo, The Winner Takes It All

5 Which song says "Take a look up the railtrack from Miami to Canada"?   'Letter From America', 'From New York To LA', 'Walking In Memphis'

6 What is the first part of the body mentione in The Beatles hit 'Hey Jude'?   Eyes, Heart, Skin

7 Which band features in 'Where Do You Go To My Lovely'?   Rolling Stones, Beach Boys, Pink Floyd

8 Who wrote "You can't plant me in your penthouse, I'm going back to my plough"?   Tim Rice, Oscar Hammerstein, Bernie Taupin

9 Which single ends "Any way the wind blows"? Unchained Melody, Help, Bohemian Rhapsody

10 What birds are mentioned in 'Somewhere Over The Rainbow'?   Bluebirds, Doves, Nightingales

ANSWERS

1. Valentino 2. To your door 3. Voodoo dolls 4. Waterloo 5. 'Letter From America' 6. Skin 7. Rolling Stones 8. Bernie Taupin 9. Bohemian Rhapsody 10. Bluebirds

QUIZ 250

• •

1 What is the name of Boycie's wife in *Only Fools And Horses*?   Millicent, Marlene, Marion

2 Which character from *Lord Of The Rings'* Elvish name is Mithrandir?   Frodo, Gandalf, Sauron

3 Which US President was assassinated in 1881? Chester Arthur, Abraham Lincoln, James Garfield

4 Which multi-billionaire married Melinda French in 1994?   Roman Abramovich, Bill Gates, John Paul Getty

5 Which group's debut album was entitled, *Boy*? U2, Boyzone, UB40

6 Which country had its 50th anniversary as a Communist state in 1999?   Russia, Hungary, China

7 What is the worlds deepest sea?   North Sea, Dead Sea, Caribbean Sea

8 Which TV series featured a boat called The Vital Spark?   *The Love Boat*, *The Tales Of Para Handy*, *The Onedin Line*

9 Carpenter, Digger and Plasterer are all varieties of which creature?   Anteater, Bee, Worm

10 What does the BA stand for with regard to the *A Team* character BA Baracus?   Big Arms, Break Away, Bad Attitude

ANSWERS

1. Marlene 2. Gandalf 3. James Garfield 4. Bill Gates 5. U2 6. China
7. Caribbean Sea 8. *The Tales Of Para Handy* 9. Bee 10. Bad Attitude

QUIZ 251

. . . .

1 Which 1999 film won five Oscars? *Armageddon*,
   As Good As It Gets, *American Beauty*

2 What is the first letter of the Hebrew alphabet?
   Abacus, Aleph, Anon

3 Which football club won the European
   Champions Cup in 1973? Arsenal, Ajax, AC Milan

4 A shrewdness is the collective noun for which
   animal? Antelope, Ape, Ant

5 Luanda is the capital of which country? Algeria,
   Albania, Angola

6 C2H5OH is the chemical formula for what?
   Aniseed, Arsenic, Alcohol

7 Which Egyptian god is depicted by the head of a
   jackal? Ares, Apollo, Anubis

8 Pink fairy and 13-banded are both species of
   what? Anchovy, Armadillo, Albatross

9 Which Scottish football club are nicknamed, The
   Honest Men? Ayr United, Aberdeen, Arbroath

10 Which sporting trophy was originally called the
   100 Guineas Cup? Ayr Gold Cup, America's Cup,
   Ashes

ANSWERS

1. *American Beauty* 2. Aleph 3. Ajax 4. Ape 5. Angola 6. Alcohol 7. Anubis
8. Armadillo 9. Ayr United 10. America's Cup

QUIZ 252

1 What is the last name of the character played by Robbie Coltrane in the TV crime drama *Cracker*? Fitzpatrick, Fitzwarren, Fitzgerald

2 Which religion's beliefs are embodied in the Four Noble Truths? Taoism, Buddhism, Hinduism

3 Who married Freddie Prinze Jnr in 2002? Angelina Jolie, Sarah Michelle Geller, Meg Ryan

4 In the sentence "They jumped over the wall" which word is the pronoun? Wall, Jumped, They

5 Which of The Magnificent Seven died in November 2002? Horst Buchholz, Yul Brynner, James Coburn

6 In which century did Leonardo da Vinci paint The Last Supper? 12th, 15th, 17th,

7 Turpentine is obtained from which tree? Rubber, Cedar, Pine

8 Who played the role of Jesus in the 1988 film *The Last Temptation Of Christ*? Mel Gibson, Tommy Lee Jones, Willem Dafoe

9 In which city is The Hunchback Of Notre Dame set? Barcelona, Paris, Venice

10 On which continent are the Atlas Mountains? Africa, Europe, South America

ANSWERS

1. Fitzgerald 2. Buddhism 3. Sarah Michelle Geller 4. They 5. James Coburn
6. 15th 7. Pine 8. Willem Dafoe 9. Paris 10. Africa

QUIZ 253

1. What did British Honduras change its name to in 1973? Benin, Belize, Basra

2. Which sport is governed by the BBBC? Basketball, Boxing, Baseball

3. What is formed by the process of ossification? Brass, Bones, Bread

4. In the Middle Ages what crime had been committed by people branded with the letter B? Blasphemy, Bigamy, Begging

5. Which city is home to the Mannekin Pis statue? Bonn, Baghdad, Brussels

6. What name is given to a citizen of Brittany? Brit, Breton, Brittanian

7. A cete is the collective noun for a group of what? Bumblebees, Badgers, Blackbirds

8. Which of the following is a former name of Istanbul? Bedouin, Belmopan, Byzantium

9. What is ballistophobia the fear of? Baths, Birds, Bullets

10. What is the most highly populated country in the world beginning with the letter B? Brazil, Benin, Bulgaria

ANSWERS

1. Belize 2. Boxing 3. Bones 4. Blasphemy 5. Brussels 6. Breton 7. Badgers
8. Byzantium 9. Bullets 10. Brazil

QUIZ 254

1 On a Monopoly board, what square lies between Vine Street and The Strand? Chance, Water Works, Free Parking

2 What type of dancing was central to the plot of the film *Billy Elliot*? Ballet, Disco, Tap

3 How many legs has a flea? 4, 6, 8

4 Which US city is known as The Golden Gate City? San Francisco, Detroit, Boston

5 Which chess piece only moves diagonally? Rook, Knight, Bishop

6 In which decade was the soccer World Cup first contested? 1920s, 1930s, 1950s

7 According to superstition, the title of which Shakespeare play should not be uttered in a theatre? *Macbeth*, *King Lear*, *Othello*

8 How were Franklin D Roosevelt and Theodore Roosevelt releated? Cousins, Brothers, Uncle and nephew

9 In which century did the 100 Years War begin? 12th, 14th, 15th

10 Which character has been played on film by Harrison Ford, Alec Baldwin and Ben Affleck? Dr Kimble, Indiana Jones, Jack Ryan

ANSWERS

1. Free Parking 2. Ballet 3. 6 4. San Francisco 5. Bishop 6. 1930s
7. *Macbeth* 8. Cousins 9. 14th 10. Jack Ryan

QUIZ 255

. . . .

1 What is a collective noun for a group of rhinoceroses?   Clout, Crash, Colony

2 What is the alternative name for the gillyflower? Carnation, Crocus, Clematis

3 What does a speleologist study?   Clouds, Cats, Caves

4 What is the name of the man eating plant belonging to the Addams Family?   Claudius, Calpurnia, Cleopatra

5 What is the middle name of Victoria Beckham? Camille, Caroline, Cecilia

6 What is the liqueur kahlua made from?   Cherries, Coffee, Cheese

7 What word is the opposite of convex? Concourse, Concave, Conform

8 Which group backed the singing 60s star Emile Ford?   Coasters, Checkmates, Cruisers

9 What does the C stand for in the name of the author CS Lewis?   Craig, Cecil, Clive

10 Which group's album Clocks won a 2003 Grammy Award?   Coldplay, Chicago, Clannad

ANSWERS

1. Crash 2. Carnation 3. Caves 4. Cleopatra 5. Caroline 6. Coffee
7. Concave 8. Checkmates 9. Clive 10. Coldplay

QUIZ 256

. . . .

1 The young of which bird is called an eyas? Eagle, Hawk, Kiwi

2 What number is sandwiched between 10 and 2 on a dartboard? 7, 15, 16,

3 Which of the following countries covers the largest area? Brazil, Canada, India

4 What is the monetary unit of Korea? Lat, Yen, Won

5 What did Lewis Edson Waterman invent in 1884? Gramophone, Electric guitar, Fountain pen

6 Who played Cher's leading man in the film *Moonstruck*? Joe Pesci, Bob Hoskins, Nicholas Cage

7 Which of the Seven Wonders of the Ancient World was located on the island of Rhodes? Hanging gardens, The Colossus, Statue of Zeus

8 In which century did the Bank of England issue Britain's first bank notes? 15th, 16th, 17th

9 What provides the staple diet of the aardvark? Fish, Snakes, Ants

10 How many US states have names that begin with a compass point? 4, 5, 6

ANSWERS

1. Hawk 2. 15 3. Canada 4. Won 5. Fountain pen 6. Nicholas Cage 7. The Colossus 8. 17th 9. Ants 10. 5

QUIZ 257

1 What is cynophobia the fear of? Dolls, Dirt, Dogs

2 Which Scottish football club are nicknamed The Parrs? Dundee Utd, Dunfermline Athletic, Dundee

3 A triton is half man and half what? Dromedary, Dragon, Dolphin

4 Which character made his cartoon debut in the 1934 animated short, *The Little Wise Hen*? Deputy Dawg, Donald Duck, Droopy

5 What was the name of the world's first cloned sheep? Daphne, Debbie, Dolly

6 What is the state capital of Delaware? Des Moines, Detroit, Dover

7 What animal does the adjective columbine refer to? Dinosaur, Duck, Dingo

8 What is Othello's wife's name in the Shakespeare play? Delores, Desdemona, Demetria

9 Joe Friday is the lead character in which TV series? *Don't Wait Up*, *Doctor At Sea*, *Dragnet*

10 Who was voted BBC Sports Personality of the Year in 1996? Darren Gough, David Beckham, Damon Hill

ANSWERS

1. Dogs 2. Dunfermline Athletic 3. Dolphin 4. Donald Duck 5. Dolly
6. Dover 7. Duck 8. Desdemona 9. *Dragnet* 10. Damon Hill

QUIZ 258

1 Which role was played by James Doohan in *Star Trek*? Chekov, Scotty, McCoy

2 What was the best selling song recorded by a woman in the 20th century? 'My Heart Will Go On', 'The Power Of Love', 'I Will Always Love You'

3 Of which state was Bill Clinton the governor in the 1980s? Arizona, Arkansas, Maine

4 Which US President is depicted on a $20 bill? John Tyler, John Quincy Adams, Andrew Jackson

5 Who disappeared flying over the South Pacific in 1937? Amy Johnson, Amelia Earhart, Jimmy Hoffa

6 What name does rap star born Curtis Jackson use? 50 Cent, 5 Dollar, 10 Bucks

7 In which capital city was Ursula Andress born? Oslo, Berne, Stockholm

8 Which comedian was born Jim Moir? Eddie Izzard, Vic Reeves, Jim Bowen

9 Which actor was the subject of a hit by the animated group Gorlillaz in 2001? Michael Caine, Clint Eastwood, Steve McQueen

10 What was second film in which Mark Hamill played Luke Skywalker? *The Empire Strikes Back*, *Return of The Jedi*, *The Phantom Menace*

ANSWERS

1. Scotty 2. 'I Will Always Love You' 3. Arkansas 4. Andrew Jackson
5. Amelia Earhart 6. 50 Cent 7. Berne 8. Vic Reeves 9. Clint Eastwood
10. *The Empire Strikes Back*

QUIZ 259

• •

1 What is the 12th letter of the Greek alphabet?
   Ma, Mo, Mu

2 Isidore is the patron saint of which European city?
   Manchester, Madrid, Milan

3 What is the collective noun for a group of crows?
   Muster, Murder, Muddle

4 What is the most highly populated city in
   Wisconsin?   Miami, Milwaukee, Madison

5 What did Percy Spencer invent in 1945?   Morse
   Code, Microwave oven, Machine gun

6 What is the longest river in the world beginning
   with the letter M?   Mississippi, Marne, Mackenzie

7 Which city is served by Linate International
   Airport?   Montreal, Milan, Marseilles

8 Which ship sailed from Plymouth to
   Massachusetts in 1620?   Morning Cloud,
   Mauretania, Mayflower

9 A barren is the collective noun for which animal?
   Mole, Moose, Mule

10 MA is the international car registration plate for
   which country?   Malta, Monaco, Morocco

ANSWERS

1. Mu 2. Madrid 3. Murder 4. Milwaukee 5. Microwave oven 6, Mississippi
7. Milan 8. Mayflower 9. Mule 10. Morocco

QUIZ 260

1 Which part of the body is affected by caries?
   Toes, Trachea, Teeth

2 What nationality is the tennis star Goran
   Ivanisevic?   American, Croatian, Swiss

3 Which doctor created The Cat In The Hat?   Dr
   Watson, Dr Seuss, Dr Barnado

4 What does the D stand for in the audio tape
   acronym DAT?   Durable, Dolby, Digital

5 In 1941 who became the first ever recipient of a
   gold disc?   Al Jolson, Glenn Miller, Judy Garland

6 Who played the role of Jerry and Daphne in the
   film *Some Like It Hot*?   Tony Curtis, Jane Russell,
   Jack Lemmon

7 Which of the following vegetables is found in a
   Waldorf salad?   Celery, Kale, Spinach

8 What is the alternative name of the Greek hero
   Ulysses?   Orpheus, Odysseus, Oliver

9 According to Shakespeare what do some achieve
   and some have thrust upon them?   Respect,
   Greatness, Fame

10 What was the title of the first talkie film?   *A Night
    To Remember*, *The Jazz Singer*, *Blackmail*

ANSWERS

1. Teeth 2. Croatian 3. Dr Seuss 4. Digital 5. Glenn Miller 6. Jack Lemmon
7. Celery 8. Odysseus 9. Greatness 10. *The Jazz Singer*

QUIZ 261

- -

1 What does the first R stand for in the name of the author JRR Tolkien?   Robert, Ronald, Ryan

2 An unkindness is the collective noun for which animal?   Robin, Raven, Rat

3 Who won a Best Director Oscar for the film *Gandhi*?   Robert Redford, Richard Attenborough, Roman Polanski

4 What nickname was given to King William II?   Rex, Rainmaker, Rufus

5 What does the R stand for in the computer acronym RAM?   Random, Regional, Radio

6 What did Robert Watson-Watt invent in 1935?   Refridgerator, Radar, Roller blades

7 In which sport is the Doggetts Coat and Badge awarded?   Rowing, Rally driving, Rugby union

8 What was the name of the torture chamber in the novel *1984*?   Room 101, Room 1001, Room 999

9 What was the European City of Culture in 2001?   Rome, Rotterdam, Rosenberg

10 What was the name of the raft in which Thor Heyerdahl crossed the Atlantic Ocean?   Red Dwarf, Ra II, Revenge

ANSWERS

1. Ronald 2. Raven 3. Richard Attenborough 4. Rufus 5. Random 6. Radar
7. Rowing 8. Room 101 9. Rotterdam 10. Ra II

QUIZ 262

1 Who wrote Down And Out In Paris And London? HG Wells, George Orwell, Charles Dickens

2 What does Dalai Lama mean in English? Chosen One, Ocean of Wisdom, Enlightened One

3 In *The Lord Of The Rings*, how many members are there in the *Fellowship of the Ring*? 9, 69, 99

4 What type of animal adopted an orphaned piglet in the film *Babe*? Fox, Sheepdog, Bull

5 Which US President survived an assassination attempt by John Schrank? Theodore Roosevelt, Jimmy Carter, Lyndon B Johnson

6 What is Margaret Houlihan's nickname in MASH? Poker Face, Hotlips, Bright Eyes

7 Who performed one armed press-ups on stage after receiving an Oscar for his role in City Slickers? Billy Crystal, Jack Palance, Martin Short

8 Who played basketball for the Chicago Bulls and baseball for the Birmingham Barons? Wilt Chamberlain, Michael Jordan, Magic Johnson

9 Which star of *Happy Days* directed *Splash*? Scott Baio, Ron Howard, Tom Bosley

10 What is the last name of the doctor that becomes the Incredible Hulk? Banner, Barnes, Bixby

ANSWERS

1. George Orwell 2. Ocean of Wisdom 3. 9 4. Sheepdog 5. Theodore Roosevelt 6. Hotlips 7. Jack Palance 8. Michael Jordan 9. Ron Howard 10. Banner

QUIZ 263

1 What is tachophobia the fear of?   Speed, Snow, Showers

2 In which country was Osama Bin Laden born? Syria, Saudi Arabia, Sudan

3 What is the 12th wedding anniversary?   Silver, Silk, Steel

4 What bird provides the last name of the pirate played by Johnny Depp in *Pirates Of The Caribbean*?   Sparrow, Swift, Swan

5 What is David Hockney known for painting? Sheep, Swimming pools, Solar eclipses

6 What nickname was bestowed upon the American Civil War general, Thomas J Jackson? Sandstorm, Stonewall, Silver Fox

7 What instrument does Zoot play in *The Muppet Show*?   Sitar, Saxophone, Sousaphone

8 What word completes the saying, "Old … never die, they just fade away"?   Soldiers, Scientists, Spinsters

9 What is the national flower of the Ukraine? Shamrock, Sunflower, Snowdrop

10 Which marine creature can turn its stomach inside out?   Swordfish, Starfish, Seahorse

ANSWERS

1. Speed 2. Saudi Arabia 3. Silk 4. Sparrow 5. Swimming pools 6. Stonewall
7. Saxophone 8. Soldiers 9. Sunflower 10. Starfish

QUIZ 264

1 What lies at the centre of the coat of arms of Ireland?   Cross, Harp, Horse

2 What animal is the symbol of the Democratic Party in the USA?   Elephant, Donkey, Beaver

3 Who recorded the album, *Don't Shoot Me I'm Only The Piano Player*?   Richard Clayderman, Elton John, Billy Joel

4 On which planet was the Great Red Spot discovered in 1665?   Mars, Jupiter, Mercury

5 By what last name is the literary character of Pippi Langstrum otherwise known?   Shortskirt, Bigboot, Longstocking

6 From which public school was James Bond expelled?   Gordonstoun, Eton, Yale

7 What did the Euro replace as the currency of Italy?   Peseta, Lire, Franc

8 What name was shared by the first four British Monarchs of the House of Hanover?   Edward, George, Henry

9 In which US city is the headquarters of Microsoft? New York, Seattle, Los Angeles

10 What type of speech is a valedictory speech? Farewell speech, Wedding speech, Political speech

ANSWERS

1. Harp 2. Donkey 3. Elton John 4. Jupiter 5. Longstocking 6. Eton 7. Lire
8. George 9. Seattle 10. Farewell speech

QUIZ 265

• •

1 What is the name of the Jester in the Shakespeare play *As You Like It*? Toby, Touchstone, Titania

2 A bale is the collective noun for a group of what? Toads, Turkeys, Turtles

3 What does an arctophilist collect? Teddy bears, Train numbers, Tricycles

4 What is the name of the American football team of Tennessee? Terriers, Titans, Tigers

5 Which terrorist organisation were the archenemy of the Men From Uncle? THRUSH, THUNDER, TAIPAN

6 What was the surname of the 27th President of the USA? Tyler, Taylor, Taft

7 How many years of marriage are celebrated in a Tin Anniversary? 2, 10, 20

8 Atticus Finch is the lead character in which novel and film? *Trilby*, *To Kill A Mockingbird*, *Three Men In A Boat*

9 What is the largest of the Canary Islands? Tunisia, Tenerife, Tierra Del Fuego

10 What is the name of Neptune's largest moon? Thebe, Thar, Triton

ANSWERS

1. Touchstone 2. Turtles 3. Teddy bears 4. Titans 5. THRUSH 6. Taft 7. 10
8. *To Kill A Mockingbird* 9. Tenerife 10. Triton

QUIZ 266

. . . .

1 Who won a Best Actor Golden Globe for his role in the film *Pulp Fiction*? John Travolta, Harvey Keitel, Bruce Willis

2 Which of the following religions was founded in the city of Philadelphia? Mormon, Amish, Quaker

3 What is Scrumpy distilled from? Pears, Apples, Potatoes

4 In which century was the Notre Dame Cathedral completed? 10th, 12th, 14th

5 Who recorded the albums Jazz and The Game? King, Duke Ellington, Queen

6 Which mountain range in Turkey shares its name with a sign of the zodiac? Gemini, Libra, Leo

7 How many eyes does a spider have? 4, 6, 8

8 In which county was Princess Diana born? Lincolnshire, Norfolk, Surrey

9 Which car manufacturer has made models called the Espero and the Laganza? Daewoo, Fiat, Honda

10 What name is given to a triangle with three sides of different sizes? Equilateral, Scalene, Isosceles

ANSWERS

1. John Travolta 2. Quaker 3. Apples 4. 14th 5. Queen 6. Taurus 7. 8.
8 Norfolk 9. Daewoo 10. Scalene

QUIZ 267

. . . .

1 What V is the goddess of the hearth in Roman mythology? Violet, Vesta, Vonda

2 What G word is the collective noun for a group of hyenas? Grin, Giggle, Guffaw

3 What is the most highly populated country in the world beginning with the letter A? Argentina, Australia, Algeria

4 What does the I stand for with regard to ZIP codes? Improvement, Investment, Interstate

5 What V provides the setting for the play *Romeo And Juliet*? Vilnius, Verona, Vienna

6 What P is the name of Adrian Mole's girlfriend? Pauline, Pandora, Petunia

7 What W is the name given to a young otter? Whelp, Warren, Wilt

8 What P is criminal slang for a safe? Paul, Patrick, Peter

9 Chester White and Berkshire are both varieties of what? Potato, Pigeon, Pig

10 According to Jewish folklore, which L was the first woman? Lilith, Lydia, Lara

ANSWERS

QUIZ 268

1 What is the military rank of James Bond?
   Admiral, Commander, Colonel

2 Who did Buster Merryfield portray in the comedy
   series *Only Fools And Horses*? Grandad, Uncle
   Albert, Trigger

3 Which drink's name is derived from the Russian
   meaning little water? Whisky, Schnapps, Vodka

4 Which Disney film featured the character of Uncle
   Remus? *Bambi*, *Song Of The South*, *The Rescuers*

5 Which kitchen implement was invented by
   Robert Yeates in 1855? Can opener, Cheese
   grater, Frying pan

6 What was sold by hokey-pokey men in the 19th
   century? Coal, Ice cream, Chestnuts

7 How many Olympic Games were hosted by
   London in the 1900s? 1, 2, 5

8 What was the nationality of Everest conqueror
   Tenzing Norgay? Japanese, Nepalese, Norwegian

9 To what animal group does the adjective piscine
   refer? Birds, Fish, Reptiles

10 What is the home city of Rossini's operatic
   character of Figaro? Florence, Seville, Turin

ANSWERS

1. Commander 2. Uncle Albert 3. Vodka 4. *Song Of The South* 5. Can
opener 6. Ice cream 7. 2 8. Nepalese 9. Fish 10. Seville

QUIZ 269

1 Which of the following is not a middle name of Princess Anne? Alice, Victoria, Louise

2 Which of the following in not a colour of ball used in the game of croquet? Green, Yellow, Black

3 Which is not a time zone in the USA? Pacific, Mountain, Southernl

4 Who of the following was not in pop group The Police? Andy Summers, Midge Ure, Sting

5 Which of the following is not a bone in the ear? Incus, Sternum, Malleus

6 Identify the star sign that is not represented by a horned creature? Taurus, Cancer, Aries

7 Which of these countries does the River Rhine not flow through? Switzerland, France, Germany

8 Which of the following countries did not reach the semi-final in the 2003 rugby union World Cup? South Africa, France, Australia

9 Which of the following is not one of the names of the Four Horsemen Of The Apocolypse? War, Death, Disease

10 Which of the following is not a middle name of Prince William? Charles, Arthur, Philip

ANSWERS

1. Victoria 2. Green 3. Southern 4. Midge Ure 5. Sternum 6. Cancer
7. France 8 South Africa 9. Disease 10, Charles

QUIZ 270

1 What is the collective noun for a group of toads? Knot, Croak, Hop

2 Who penned the autobiography, The First Four Minutes? Sebastian Coe, Alexander Graham Bell, Roger Bannister

3 Who was flattened by Dorothy's house in The Wizard Of Oz? Tin Man, Wicked Witch of the East, Scarecrow

4 Who wrote 'This Is My Song', a hit for Petula Clark? Stan Laurel, Buster Keaton, Charlie Chaplin

5 The Ancient city of Sparta was located in which modern day country? Peru, Turkey, Greece

6 Which American Indian tribe did Crazy Horse belong to? Sioux, Apache, Navaho

7 Who did Alice Tinker marry in The Vicar Of Dibley? Frank Pickle, Hugo Horton, Owen Newitt

8 What was Samoa called prior to 1997? Southern Samoa, Northern Samoa, Western Samoa

9 What was the name of the ranch in the TV western Bonanza? Walnut Grove, Ponderosa, Shiloh Ranch

10 What highway did Bob Dylan revisit in the title of a best selling album? 19, 57, 61

ANSWERS

1. Knot 2. Roger Bannister 3. Wicked Witch of the East 4. Charlie Chaplin
5. Greece 6. Sioux 7. Hugo Horton 8. Western Samoa 9. Ponderosa 10. 61

QUIZ 271

- -

1 In which city do the space age cartoon family The Jetsons live?   Moon City, Rocket City, Orbit City

2 In which city is the headquarters of the Football Association?   Lancaster, London, Leicester

3 In which city was the film *Basic Instinct* set? Kansas City, San Francisco, Phoenix

4 In which city was the Coca Cola Company founded in 1892?   Houston, Memphis, Atlanta

5 Which fictional city is home to the offices of the *Daily Planet* newspaper?   Mega City One, Metropolis, Smallville

6 In which European city is the Oktober Fest Beet Festival?   Brussels, Munich, Warsaw

7 What is the name of the hill that overlooks the castle in the city of Edinburgh?   David's Bench, Arthur's Seat, Charlie's Couch

8 Barcelona,is the capital of which Spanish region? Andalusia, Basque region,Catalonia

9 Which city is home to the University of Arizona? Fort Worth,Baltimore, Tucson

10 What is Latvia's capital city?   Riga, Tallinn, Split

ANSWERS

1. Orbit City 2. London 3. San Francisco 4. Atlanta 5. Metropolis 6. Munich
7. Arthur's Seat 8. Catalonia 9. Tucson 10. Riga

QUIZ 272

1 Who is the owner of The Magic Roundabout?
   Florence, Mr Rusty, Dougal

2 Which company launched the Play Station in
   1994? Atari, Sony, Sega

3 In what year did the London Eye observatory
   wheel open in London? 1999, 2000, 2001

4 What was the nationality of the men that
   invented Lego? Dutch, Danish, Australian

5 What did the architect Frank Lloyd Wright once
   describe as, chewing gum for the eyes?
   Television, Magazines, Computer games

6 What type of vehicle is a Vespa? Train, Motor
   scooter, Hot air balloon

7 In what decade were Blackpool's illuminations
   first lit? 1860s, 1870s, 1880s

8 What sport takes place in a velodrome? Cycling,
   Horse racing, Ice skating

9 What year marked the climax of the Oscar
   winning film, *Chariots Of Fire*? 1924, 1928, 1932

10 For which football club did Bobby Moore spend
    the majority of his playing career? Fulham,
    Arsenal, West Ham

ANSWERS

1. Mr Rusty 2. Sony 3. 2000 4. Danish 5. Television 6. Motor scooter
7. 1870s 8. Cycling 9. 1924 10. West Ham

QUIZ 273

. . . .

1 What is the more common name for a natatorium? Greenhouse, Swimming pool, Aquarium

2 What is the pen name of Barbara Vine? Dorothy L Sayers, Ruth Rendell, JK Rowling

3 What is the alternative name for an avocado? Python pear, Kiwi pear, IAlligator pear

4 In the plant world, how is the delphinium otherwise known? Larkspur, Bluebell, Hyacinth

5 What is another name for the monk fish? Whale shark, Tiger shark, Angel shark

6 Which London street is known as, The Street of Ink? Bow Street, Harley Street, Fleet Street

7 By what one word name is the model Lesley Hornby better known? Caprice, Twiggy, Jordan

8 What is the alternative name for okra in the plant world? Man's toes, Baby's breath, Ladies fingers

9 In the calendar year how is St Sylvester's Day more commonly known? Good Friday, New Years Eve, Boxing Day, April Fools Day

10 How is Ariel otherwise known in the title of a Disney animated film? *The Little Mermaid*, *Sleeping Beauty*, *Pocahontas*

ANSWERS

1. Swimming pool 2. Ruth Rendell 3. Alligator pear 4. Larkspur 5. Angel shark 6. Fleet Street 7. Twiggy 8. Ladies fingers 9. New Years Eve 10. *The Little Mermaid*

QUIZ 274

1. Which TV series was set at Slade Prison? *Porridge, Prisoner Cell Block H, Bad Girls*

2. What is the name of the American counterpart of the Action Man doll? GI Jed, GI Joe, GI Jack

3. What is world's largest coral reef? Great Big Reef, Great Barrier Reef, Great Wall Reef

4. What was *The Guardian* newspaper once called? *The Glasgow Guardian, The Manchester Guardian, The Liverpool Guardian*

5. Who designed The Rocket train in 1829? James Watt, Richard Trevithick, George Stephenson

6. At which race course is Red Rum buried? Haydock, Aintree, Epsom

7. What mathematical aid was invented in 1622? Logarithms, Binary system, Slide rule

8. Which Presidents name is depicted on the Apollo 11 moon plaque? Lyndon B Johnson, Richard Nixon, George Washington

9. Which country hosted soccer's 2004 European Nations Championships? Italy, France, Portugal

10. When Jack Palance played the villain, who played the hero? Alan Ladd, John Wayne, Audie Murphy

ANSWERS

1. *Porridge* 2. GI Joe 3. Great Barrier Reef 4. *The Manchester Guardian*
5. George Stephenson 6. Aintree 7. Slide rule 8. Richard Nixon 9. Portugal
10. Alan Ladd

QUIZ 275

Identify the groups that link each trio of pop hits

1   'Live Forever', 'Roll With It', 'All Around The World'
    The Jam, Oasis, Blur

2   'The Carnival Is Over', 'A World Of Our Own',
    'Georgy Girl'   The Searchers, The Seekers, The New
    Seekers

3   'Hello Happiness', 'There Goes My First Love',
    'Saturday Night At The Movies'   Delfonics, The
    Drifters, Detroit Emeralds

4   'House Of The Rising Sun', 'I'm Crying', 'Its My Life'
    The Byrds, The Turtles, The Animals

5   'All Or Nothing', 'My Minds Eye', 'Hey Girl'   Small
    Faces, The Equals, Talking Heads

6   'Lonely This Christmas', 'The Cat Crept In', 'Oh Boy'
    Wizzard, Sweet, Mud

7   'ABC', 'Doctor My Eyes', 'I Want You Back'   Bay City
    Rollers, The Osmonds, Jackson Five

8   'Communication', 'Lifeline', 'Through The Barricades'
    Duran Duran, Spandau Ballet, Talk Talk

9   'Angelo', 'Figaro', 'United We Stand'   The Shadows,
    Brotherhood Of Man, Abba

10 'Sound Of The Underground', 'Jump', 'Stay Another
    Day'   The Spice Girls, Girls Aloud, Girlschool

ANSWERS

1. Oasis 2. The Seekers 3. The Drifters 4. The Animals 5. Small Faces 6. Mud
7. Jackson Five 8. Spandau Ballet 9. Brotherhood Of Man 10. Girls Aloud

QUIZ 276

1. What does the Statue of Liberty hold in her right hand? Book, Torch, Sword

2. What does the C stand for in the news network CNN? Cable, Cosmopolitan, Corporate

3. In which 1996 film did Michelle Pfeiffer fall in love with Robert Redford? *Up Close And Personal*, *Dangerous Liaisons*, *One Fine Day*

4. Which city is served by Ataturk Airport? Tunis, Cairo, Istanbul

5. Which record label released the song 'Here In My Heart' by Al Martino? Decca, Capitol, Sun

6. When Gary Oldman played Dracula who played Van Helsing? Hugh Jackman, Anthony Hopkins, Timothy Dalton

7. The world's first electric washing machine was named after which god? Zeus, Jupiter, Thor

8. Which US state is home to Beverly Hills? Florida, Texas, California

9. In the children's nursery rhyme, where did the fine lady ride upon a white horse? Gloucester, York, Banbury Cross

10. Which company introduced tea bags to Great Britain? Typhoo, Tetley, PG Tips

ANSWERS

1. Torch 2. Cable 3. *Up Close And Personal* 4. Istanbul 5. Capitol
6. Anthony Hopkins 7. Thor 8. California 9. Banbury Cross 10. Tetley

QUIZ 277

Identify the film stars that played each group of three characters on film

1 Lorelei Lee, Amanda Dell, Sugar Kane Kowalczyk
   Mae West, Audrey Hepburn, Marilyn Monroe

2 Thomas Crown, James Bond, Robinson Crusoe
   David Niven, Sean Connery, Pierce Brosnan

3 Sally Albright, Captain Emma Walden, Mary
   Hemingway   Bette Midler, Meg Ryan, Meryl Streep

4 Proximo, Bill Sikes, Athos   Richard Harris, Kiefer
   Sutherland, Oliver Reed

5 Titania, Catwoman, Susie Diamond   Joan Collins,
   Michelle Pfeiffer, Glenn Close

6 Annie Paradis, Kay Corleone, Annie Hall   Diane
   Keaton, Talia Shire, Goldie Hawn

7 Miranda Hillard, Mrs Gump, Norma Rae   Jessica
   Lange, Jodie Foster, Sally Field

8 Mace Windu, John Shaft, Jules Winnfield   Wesley
   Snipes, Eddie Murphy, Samuel L Jackson

9 Jack Carter, Judge Dredd, Gabe Walker   Bruce
   Willis, Sylvester Stallone, Jean Claude Van Damme

10 John Profumo, Richard III, Gandalf   Peter Cushing,
   Ian McKellan, Christopher Lee

ANSWERS

1. Marilyn Monroe 2. Pierce Brosnan 3. Meg Rya 4. Oliver Reed 5. Michelle
Pfeiffer 6. Diane Keaton 7. Sally Field 8. Samuel L Jackson 9. Sylvester
Stallone 10. Ian McKellan

QUIZ 278

• •

1 What is the name of the pet dog of Dennis The Menace? Spike, Gnasher, Yeller

2 In which city did Ma Baker live, according to the lyrics of the Boney M song? Denver, Chicago, Boston

3 Who is described as little in the title of a Charles Dickens novel? Dorritt, Nell, Barnaby

4 By Venetian law, all gondolas must be painted what colour? Gold, Black, Green

5 Who directed the film *Alien*? John Carpenter, Tony Scott, Ridley Scott

6 In what month does the astrological sign Aquarius end? January, February, September

7 What name is given to the home of a lion? Lair, Kingdom, Den

8 Which river is spanned by Britain's longest suspension bridge? Clyde, Humber, Severn

9 Which Hollywood star played Danny Wilde in the 1970s action series *The Persuaders*? Kirk Douglas, Roger Moore, Tony Curtis

10 In the USA, what is the theatrical equivalent of an Oscar? Edgar, Tony, Emmy

ANSWERS

1. Gnasher 2. Chicago 3. Dorritt 4. Black 5. Ridley Scott 6. February 7. Den
8. Humber 9. Tony Curtis 10. Tony

QUIZ 279

Identify the actor who played each group of three characters on TV

1 Peter Mayle, Henry Willows, Monsignor Renard
Michael Kitchen, Kevin Whately, John Thaw

2 Amanda Ripley, Geraldine Granger, Alice Putkin
Lisa Riley, Jane Horrocks, Emma Chambers

3 Albert Stroller, Harry Rule, Napoleon Solo   Robert
Wagner, Robert Vaughn, Patrick Macnee

4 Uriah Heep, Gary Sparrow, Rodney Trotter   Bob
Hoskins, David Jason, Nicholas Lyndhurst

5 Auntie Wainwright, Granny Trellis, Mrs Stanley
Ogden   Kathy Staff, Thora Hird, Jean Alexander

6 Abby Wallace, Cindy Beale, Nicki Williams   Tina
Hobley, Lorraine Chase, Michelle Collins

7 Clarence Sale, Norman Stanley Fletcher,
Plantaganet Evans   John Cleese, Ronnie Barker,
Ronnie Corbett

8 DS Bailey, Eddie Yeats, Vernon Scripps   Jack
Smethurst, Bill Maynard, Geoffrey Hughes

9 Ivanhoe, Brett Sinclair, Simon Templar   Roger
Moore, Sean Bean, Martin Shaw

10 Donna Sinclair, Patsy Stone, Mrs Peacock Joanna
Lumley, Felicity Kendall, Jennifer Saunders

ANSWERS

1. John Thaw 2. Dawn French 3. Robert Vaughn 4. Nicholas Lyndhurst
5. Jean Alexander 6. Michelle Collins 7. Ronnie Barker 8. Geoffrey Hughes
9. Roger Moore 10. Joanna Lumley

QUIZ 280

- -

1 What is the fifth planet from the sun?   Neptune, Saturn, Jupiter

2 In which sport was Tonya Harding involved in an assault scandal on a rival in 1994? Tennis, Ice skating, Netball

3 What is the world's deepest ocean?   Indian, Atlantic, Pacific

4 Whose official fan club is called, The Sons Of The Desert?   Peter O'Toole, Laurel & Hardy, Omar Sharif

5 In what year was the worlds first test tube baby born?   1958, 1968, 1978

6 How many prime numbers fall between 10 and 20?   2, 3, 4

7 Which musical featured the song, 'Hello Young Lovers'?   *Grease, West Side Story, The King And I*

8 Who was the Vice President to John F Kennedy? Bobby Kennedy, Lyndon B Johnson, Richard Nixon

9 Where on a car is an inertia reel found? Windscreen wipers, Seat belt, Steering wheel

10 Who is credited with inventing the petrol driven motor car?   Henry Ford, Louis Renault, Karl Benz

ANSWERS

1. Jupiter 2. Ice skating 3. Pacific 4. Laurel & Hardy 5. 1978 6. 4 7. *The King And I* 8. Lyndon B Johnson 9. Seat belt 10. Karl Benz

QUIZ 281

Identify the writer who links each trio of novels

1. *In Search Of Castaways, The Mysterious Island, Five Weeks In A Balloon*   Jules Verne, Arthur Conan Doyle, Edgar Allan Poe

2. *Northanger Abbey, Sense & Sensibility, Mansfield Park*   Alice Walker, Mary Norton, Jane Austen

3. *The Dead Zone, Christine, Salems Lot*   Stephen King, James Herbert, Dean Koontz

4. *Lucky Jim, The Old Devils, Colonel Sun*   Dennis Wheatley, Kingsley Amis, Charles Kingsley

5. *Treasure Island, Kidnapped, The Ebb Tibe*   Walter Scott, John Buchan, Robert Louis Stevenson

6. *The Count Of Monte Cristo, The Three Musketeers, The Man In The Iron Mask*   Alexandre Dumas, Victor Hugo, Umberto Eco

7. *The Rainbow, Women In Love, The Plumed Serpent*   Tom Wolfe, Iain Banks, DH Lawrence

8. *Score, Polo, Riders*   Barbara Cartland, Jilly Cooper, Virginia Andrews

9. *A Time To Kill, The Firm, The Client*   Michael Crichton, John Grisham, Tom Clancy,

10. *Kim, The Light That Failed, The Jungle Book*   Rudyard Kipling, Diane Fossey, Joy Adamson

ANSWERS

QUIZ 282

. . . .

1 Who was elected Governor of California in 1966? Jimmy Carter, John Wayne, Ronald Reagan

2 Which musical instrument is assembled and repaired by a bellyman?   Harp, Piano, Guitar

3 What method of transport connects the films *Speed* and *The Gauntlet*?   Train, Motorbike, Bus

4 Which film featured the sinking of a vessel called The Orca?   *Master And Commander*, *Pirates Of The Caribbean*, *Jaws*

5 Which of the following is not a room in the board game of Cluedo?   Attic, Conservatory, Ballroom

6 Which long running radio show is introduced by a piece of music entitled, By The Sleepy Lagoon? The Archers, Desert Island Discs, Family Favourites

7 In which city was the worlds first restaurant opened in 1765?   New York, Paris, Moscow

8 On which Greek island was Hippocrates born? Crete, Kos, Samos

9 In 1983 which company launched the first lap top computer?   Apple, Tandy, Microsoft

10 Which element has the chemical symbol No? Nobelium, Nitrogen, Neon

ANSWERS

1. Ronald Reagan 2. Piano 3. Bus 4. *Jaws* 5. Attic 6. Desert Island Discs
7. Paris 8. Kos 9. Tandy 10. Nobelium

QUIZ 283

• •

1 What colour are Smurfs?   Yellow, Blue, Green

2 What is the name of the policeman in the *Noddy* stories?   PC Plod, PC Pat, PC World

3 What type of animal is Manny in the animated movie *Ice Age*?   Seal, Mammoth, Vulture

4 Which clown has been assisted on TV by Side Show Bob and Side Show Mel?   Charlie the Clown, Krusty The Clown, Crumb the Clown

5 What household item was swallowed by a crocodile in *Peter Pan*?   Frying pan, Alarm clock, Wine glass

6 What type of animal is Toto in *The Wizard Of Oz*? Lion, Monkey, Dog

7 What is the name of the rabbit in Disney's *Bambi*? Jumper, Thumper, Grumper

8 Who lives in a dustbin in *Sesame Street*?   Ernie, Oscar, Bert

9 "Boom Boom" is the catchphrase of which childrens TV character?   Basil Brush, Dangermouse, Hong Kong Phooey

10 What type of animal is Splinter, the tutor of the *Teenage Mutant Ninja Turtles*?   Owl, Otter, Rat

ANSWERS

QUIZ 284

1. Graphite is composed of which element? Gold, Lead, Carbon

2. Who played the President of the USA in the film *Primary Colors*? Michael Douglas, John Travolta, Gene Hackman

3. In South Africa what is known as The Mother City? Durban, Pretoria, Cape Town

4. What is the official national sport of Indonesia? Judo, Table tennis, Badminton

5. Which Hollywood icon was born John Carter? Clark Gable, Steve McQueen, Charlton Heston

6. Which weekday was named after the Norse god of thunder? Wednesday, Thursday, Saturday

7. In which century did the highwayman Dick Turpin die? 15th, 16th, 18th

8. Which European capital city stands on the River Aare? Berne, Berlin, Vienna

9. What causes the hum of the hummingbird? Mouth, Wings, Gizzard

10. What title did Priyanka Chopra win in November 2000? The Turner Prize, Miss World, Nobel Prize for Literature

ANSWERS

1. Carbon 2. John Travolta 3. Cape Town 4. Badminton 5. Charlton Heston
6. Thursday 7. 18th 8. Berne 9. Wings 10. Miss World

QUIZ 285

Identify the football clubs from their home grounds and nicknames

1 Pride Park and The Rams   Grimsby Town, Boston United, Derby County

2 Selhurst Park and The Eagles   Crystal Palace, Brighton, Hull City

3 Vicarage Road and The Hornets   Brentford, Crewe Alexandra, Watford

4 The Hawthorns and The Baggies   Peterborough United, Arsenal, West Bromwich Albion

5 Plainmoor and The Gulls   Millwall, Torquay United, Norwich City

6 The Reebok Stadium and The Trotters. Ipswich Town, Bolton Wanderers, Rotherham United

7 The McAlpine Stadium and The Terriers   Huddersfield Town, Luton Town, Mansfield Town

8 Home Park and The Pilgrims   Preston North End, Plymouth Argyle, Port Vale

9 Memorial Ground and The Pirates   Bristol Rovers, Swansea City, Coventry City

10 The Britannia Stadium and The Potters   Rochdale, Stoke City, Everton

ANSWERS

1. Derby County 2. Crystal Palace 3. Watford 4. West Bromwich Albion
5. Torquay United 6. Bolton Wanderers 7. Huddersfield Town 8. Plymouth
Argyle 9. Bristol Rovers 10. Stoke City

QUIZ 286

. . . .

1 Which vegetable is served with eggs in the dish Egg Florentine? Turnip, Spinach, Carrot

2 Elmo Lincoln was the first actor to play who on film? *Dracula*, *Tarzan*, *Superman*

3 On which continent is the country of Angola found? Asia, Africa, Europe

4 What does the G stand for in the Roald Dahl novel *The BFG*? Giant, Gorgon, Gremlin

5 Which US state had several vote recounts to determine the 2000 Presidential Election result? Alaska, Montana, Florida

6 Which South American country shares a border with Panama? Bolivia, Colombia, Uruguay

7 In which sport do competitors use the telemark position? Parachuting, Ski jumping, Gymnastics

8 Which country is separated from Spain by the Straits of Gibraltar? Portugal, Morocco, Tunisia

9 Which actor played the title role in the film *Cool Hand Luke*? George Kennedy, Paul Newman, James Caan

10 Which European nation were surprise winners of the gold medal for men's basketball at the 1980 Olympics? Germany, Yugoslavia, Belgium

ANSWERS

1. Spinach 2. *Tarzan* 3. Africa 4. Giant (Big Friendly Giant) 5. Florida
6. Colombia 7. Ski jumping 8. Morocco 9. Paul Newman 10. Yugoslavia

QUIZ 287

. . . .

What name is given to a young …

1 Goose? Gosling, Squab, Gander

2 Spider? Spiderling, Spiderspit, Spiderkindle

3 Hare? Kit, Warren, Leveret

4 Cranefly? Leatherjacket, Silkshirt, Clothcap

5 Herring? Smolt, Parr, Whitebait

6 Pike? Joe, Jim, Jack

7 Gnat? Gloworm, Bloodworm, Silkworm

8 Eagle? Elver, Eagling, Eaglet

9 Elephant? Pup, Calf, Lamb

10 Platypus? Muggle, Snuggle, Puggle

ANSWERS

1. Gosling 2. Spiderling 3. Leveret 4. Leatherjacket 5. Whitebait 6. Jack
7. Bloodworm 8. Eaglet 9. Calf 10. Puggle

QUIZ 288

1 What does a radiologist study? Pop music, X Rays, The Sun

2 Which nation won the 1986 soccer World Cup? Italy, Brazil, Argentina

3 The Gulf Of Venice is the most northerly point of which sea? Baltic Sea, Adriatic Sea, Caspian Sea

4 In Greek mythology, who was the first woman on Earth? Helen, Pandora, Andromeda

5 In which coutry was the film *Bridge On The River Kwai* set? Thailand, India, China

6 How many points is a cannon worth in the game of billiards? 1, 2, 6

7 What is the occupation of Bert in the film and novel *Mary Poppins*? Chimney sweep, Baker, Carpenter

8 What did the F stand for in the name of the explorer Robert F Scott? Forrest, Falcon, Frederick

9 Cava wine originates from which country? Malta, France, Spain

10 What type of beans are used to make baked beans? Haricot, Broad, Butter

ANSWERS

1. X Rays 2. Argentina 3. Adriatic Sea 4. Pandora 5. Thailand 6. 2
7. Chimney sweep 8. Falcon 9. Spain 10. Haricot

QUIZ 289

Which song provided the first number one hit for the following recording artists?

1. Boyzone 'No Matter What', 'Father and Son', 'Words'

2. David Bowie 'Lets Dance', 'Jean Genie', 'Space Oddity'

3. Madonna 'Vogue', 'Into The Groove', 'Like A Prayer'

4. The Jam 'Going Underground', 'Start', 'Beat Surrender'

5. Dexy's Midnight Runners 'Come On Eileen', 'Because Of You', 'Geno'

6. Blondie 'The Tide Is High', 'Maria', 'Heart Of Glass'

7. The Spice Girls 'Two Much', 'Wannabe', 'Mama'

8. George Michael 'A Different Corner', 'Faith', 'Careless Whisper'

9. T Rex 'Jeepster', 'Telegram Sam', 'Hot Love'

10. The Bee Gees 'Jive Talking', 'How Deep Is Your Love', 'Massachusetts'

ANSWERS

1. 'Words' 2. 'Space Oddity' 3. 'Into The Groove' 4. 'Going Underground'
5. 'Geno' 6. 'Heart Of Glass' 7. 'Wannabe' 8. 'Careless Whisper' 9. 'Hot Love'
10. 'Massachusetts'

QUIZ 290

1 The Joad family feature in which novel by John Steinbeck? *Heart Of Darkness*, *The Grapes Of Wrath*, *East Of Eden*

2 How does Moulin Rouge translate into English? Red Admiral, Red Windmill, Red Sea

3 IN which country is Mount Eiger? Austria, Norway, Switzerland

4 Who played Mr Harmon in *Are You Being Served*? Alfie Bass, John Inman, Arthur·English

5 In which county is Catterick race course? Staffordshire, Lancashire, North Yorkshire

6 What is the legal age for purchasing alcohol in the USA? 16, 18, 21

7 The Euro is divided into 100 what? Cents, Pennies, Centimes

8 In which century did Isaac Newton die? 16th, 17th, 18th

9 According to the proverb, what do mighty oaks grow from? Short seeds, Little acorns, Tiny twigs

10 In 1936, who was crowned Miss Hungary when she was just sixteen years old? Marlene Dietrich, Zsa Zsa Gabor, Audrey Hepburn

ANSWERS

1. *The Grapes Of Wrath* 2. Red Windmill 3. Switzerland 4. Arthur English
5. North Yorkshire 6. 21 7. Cents 8. 18th 9. Little acorns 10. Zsa Zsa Gabor

QUIZ 291

. . . .

1 What is the name of Martin Crane's pet dog in the US sitcom *Frasier*?   Spike, Eddie, Floyd

2 Which American football club are known as The Jaguars?   Carolina, Jacksonville, Kansas City

3 What was the name of Blue Peter's first dog? Jason, Petra, Shep

4 What is the name of the dog, one of Enid Blyton's Famous Five?   Jock, Timmy, Scamper

5 Which cartoon feline first appeared in a 1945 animation entitled, *Life With Feathers*?   Sylvester, Garfield, The Cat In The Hat

6 What is the name of Little Orphan Annie's dog? Brandy, Sandy, Mandy

7 Which cartoon canine accompanies Musky Muskrat?   Deputy Dawg, Snoopy, Huckleberry Hound

8 Who created the fictional cat, Old Deuteronomy? Jack London, Joy Adamson, TS Eliot

9 What is the name of the canine sidekick of Dick Dastardly?   Goofy, Muttley, Droopy

10 Which Disney animation features Duchess and Thomas O'Malley?   *101 Dalmatians*, *The Aristocats*, *The Fox And The Hound*

ANSWERS

1. Eddie 2. Jacksonville 3. Petra 4. Timmy 5. Sylvester 6. Sandy 7. Deputy Dawg 8. TS Eliot 9. Muttley 10. *The Aristocats*

QUIZ 292

• •

1 In which country was instant coffee invented?
   USA, Switzerland, Brazil

2 Which vitamin is produced in human skin on
   exposure to sunlight?   C, D, K

3 Which country's coast witnessed the Battle of
   Trafalgar?   Spain, France, Denmark

4 What was the only animal aloud to enter temples
   in Ancient Rome?   Cat, Dog, Pig

5 Who narrated the 1964 film *Zulu*?   Richard
   Burton, Michael Caine, Stanley Baker

6 Which was the first US state to be named after a
   US born civilian?   Louisianna, Maryland,
   Washington

7 What is the most common consonant in the
   names of the seven days of the week?   D, S, Y

8 From which language did the word albino
   originate?   Arabic, Portuguese, Spanish

9 In 1960 which company introduced the world's
   first ready salted crisps?   Golden Wonder, Walkers,
   Smiths

10 Whci city is home to the Hudson and East rivers?
   Dublin, Glasgow, New York

ANSWERS

1. Switzerland 2. D 3. Spain 4. Cat 5. Richard Burton 6. Washington 7. D
8. Portuguese 9. Golden Wonder 10. New York

QUIZ 293

Identify the TV show from each group of characters

1. Barbara, Jim, Dave, Denise, Anthony *The Sopranos, The Brady Bunch, The Royle Family*

2. Atlanta, Marina, Titan *Stingray, The Man From Atlantis, Space 1999*

3. Sergeant Lucy Bates, Officer Renko, Lieutenant Buntz *Cagney & Lacey, Hill Street Blues, Kojak*

4. Dan Connor, Becky Connor, DJ Connor *Happy Days, Roseanne, Diff'rent Strokes*

5. Woody Boyd, Cliff Clavin, Norm Peterson *Seinfeld, Ellen, Cheers*

6. Sergeant Wilson, Private Walker, Private Pike *The Army Game, Bootsie & Snudge, Dad's Army*

7. Margo, Jerry, Barbara, Tom *The Good Life, Keeping Up Appearances, Rising Damp*

8. Captain Crane, Admiral Nelson, Lieutenant Commander Morton *Sharpe, Star Trek: The Next Generation, Voyage To The Bottom Of The Sea*

9. Ben Cartwright, Adam Cartwright, Hoss Cartwright *Bonanza, The High Chaparral, The Virginian*

10. Renee Raddick, Richard Fish, Ling Woo *LA Law, Six Feet Under, Ally McBeal*

ANSWERS

1. *The Royle Family* 2. *Stingray* 3. *Hill Street Blues* 4. *Roseanne* 5. *Cheers*
6. *Dad's Army* 7. *The Good Life* 8. *Voyage To The Bottom Of The Sea*
9. *Bonanza* 10. *Ally McBeal*

QUIZ 294

• •

1 In which capital city is Oscar Wilde buried?
   Stockholm, Paris, Rome

2 Which Shakespeare play opens with the line,
   "Now is the winter of our discontent"? *Richard III,*
   King Lear, Macbeth

3 Where in the human body are the hammer and
   anvil located? Brain, Ear, Throat

4 What did Fibre·K change its name to in 1959?
   Nylon, Lycra, Velcro

5 Amnesia is the loss of what? Smell, Taste, Memory

6 What is the cube root of 512? 6, 7, 8

7 In which sport is Pierre Luigi Collina a noted
   official? Football, Boxing, Rugby union

8 Who led the Charge Of The Light Brigade? Lord
   Derby, Earl Of Cardigan, Marquis of Queensbury

9 How many Wimbledon Singles titles did Boris
   Becker win? 1, 3, 5

10 In which building in Washington DC do the US
   Congress meet? Pentagon, Capitol, White House

ANSWERS

1. Paris 2. *Richard III* 3. Ear 4. Lycra 5. Memory 6 8 7. Football
8. Earl Of Cardigan 9. 3 10. Capitol

QUIZ 295

1 In which 1969 film did Richard Burton play Henry VIII? *Carry On Henry*, *Anne Of A Thousand Days*, *The Lion In Winter*

2 Which monarch's statue stands on a traffic island outside Buckingham Palace? Queen Victoria, George V, Edward VII

3 Which king was the husband of Marie Antoinette? Louis XVI, Louis X, Louis XVIII

4 Who topped the UK singles charts with the song, 'Stand By Me'? Ben E King, Carole King, Evelyn Champagne King

5 Which herb derives its name from the Greek word for king? Basil, Oregano, Sage

6 Who did Queen Elizabeth II succeed as monarch? Queen Elizabeth I, George VI, Edward VI

7 In which country was Richard the Lionheart killed? Scotland, France, Ireland

8 Which wife of Henry VIII had eleven fingers? Anne Boleyn, Catherine Parr, Anne Of Cleves

9 Which 11th century king was known as the Confessor? Harold, William, Edward

10 Which of the following is not a royal house in the British monarchy? Stuart, Savoy, Plantagenet

ANSWERS

1. *Anne Of A Thousand Days* 2. Queen Victoria 3. Louis XVI 4. Ben E King
5. Basil 6. George VI 7. France 8. Anne Boleyn 9. Edward 10. Savoy

QUIZ 296

• •

1 In the opening line of which novel did the clock strike thirteen? *1984, The Time Machine, Journey To The Centre Of The Earth*

2 Which car company was founded by Colin Chapman? Jaguar, Lotus, BMW

3 What is the US military academy in New York State called? East Point, North Point, West Point

4 Who plays the role of DCI Barnaby in *Midsomer Murders*? John Nettles, Trevor Eve, David Jason

5 In what decade was the bikini introduced to the public? 1930s, 1940s, 1950s

6 Which Shakespeare play features the line, "If music be the food of love play on"? *Twelfth Night, As You Like It, Romeo And Juliet*

7 Where was the worlds first tilting bridge built in 2001? Luton, Chelmsford, Gateshead

8 In which comedy series did a lead character often exclaim, "I have a cunning plan"? *The A Team, Blackadder, Dads Army*

9 Where was Britain's first nuclear power station built? Calder Hall, Greenwich, Falkirk

10 Which was the first London department store to install an escalator? Hamleys, Harrods, Selfridges

ANSWERS

1. *1984* 2. Lotus 3. West Point 4. John Nettles 5. 1940s 6. *Twelfth Night*
7. Gateshead 8. *Blackadder* 9. Calder Hall 10. Harrods

QUIZ 297

1 Which war was ended in 1856 by the Treaty of Paris? Crimean, Boer, Opium

2 Who is the Roman god of war? Jupiter, Mars, Saturn

3 Which country was embroiled in a civil war from 1936 to 1939? Canada, Spain, Turkey

4 Which country was invaded by Iraq in 1990? Iran, Kuwait, Israel

5 Near which Scottish city was the Battle of Culloden fought? Aberdeen, Glasgow, Inverness

6 At which battle did Rome defeat the forces of Anthony and Cleopatra? Troy, Rubicon, Actium

7 Members of whose gang were killed in the Gunfight At The OK Corral? Hole In The Wall Gang, Clanton Gang, The Regulators

8 The Battle of Bull Run was fought during which conflict? US Civil War, Korean War, Vietnam War

9 Where did William Wallace defeat the forces of Edward I in 1297? Dunbar, Sedgemoor, Stirling Bridge

10 In which country was the Battle of the Somme fought in World War I? Germany, Poland, France

ANSWERS

1. Crimean 2. Mars 3. Spain 4. Kuwait 5. Inverness 6. Actium 7. Clanton Gang 8. US Civil War 9. Stirling Bridger 10. France

QUIZ 298

1 In which state is the gambling oasis of Las Vegas?
   Texas, Nevada, Arizona

2 In his will, William Shakespeare left his wife his
   second best what?   Bed, Horse, Pen

3 What animal travels in mobs under the leadership
   of a boomer?   Kangaroo, Reindeers, Hyenas

4 Who founded the American Safety Razor
   Company in 1902? Thomas Wilkinson, King Camp
   Gillette, Jacob Schick

5 What does a cordwainer make for a living?
   Wheels, Hats, Shoes

6 What was the nationality of the man after whom
   nicotine was named?   French, Dutch, Italian

7 In which athletic event has Steve Backley
   represented Britain?   Shot putt, Javelin, Discus

8 In 1990 what became the worlds first space
   telescope?   Toil, Trubble, Hubble

9 To what wild cat does the adjective pardine refer?
   Polecat, Tiger, Leopard

10 Which film introduced cinema goers to a
   Volkswagen called Herbie?   *Monte Carlo Or Bust*,
   The Love Bug, *The Great Race*

ANSWERS

1. Nevada 2. Bed 3. Kangaroo 4. King Camp Gillette 5. Shoes 6. French
7. Javelin 8. Hubble 9. Leopard 10. *The Love Bug*

QUIZ 299

1 Which siblings had a hit with the song, 'I'm In The Mood For Dancing'?   The Nolan Sisters, The Andrews Sisters, Sister Sledge

2 What is the father of the Tracy brothers named in Thunderbirds?   Jeremy, John, Jeff

3 Who is the mother of the singer Lorna Luft? Elizabeth Taylor, Judy Garland, Mary Pickford

4 What was the surname of the central family in the TV sitcom *2.4 Children*?   Carter, Porter, Butcher

5 Who was the Biblical father of Esau and Jacob? Noah, Isaac, Abraham

6 What was the name of the Kray twins mother? Hyacinth, Fleur, Violet

7 How is Princess Anne related to Viscount Linley? Cousin, Aunt, Sister

8 Who is the father of Tiny Tim in A Christmas Carol? Jacob Marley, Ebenezer Scrooge, Bob Cratchit

9 What is the name of Tony Blair's first born son? Euan, Leo, James

10 What is the name of Margaret Thatcher's daughter?   Carol, Anne, Julia

ANSWERS

1 The Nolan Sisters 2. Jeff 3. Judy Garland 4. Porter 5. Isaac 6. Violet
7. Cousin 8. Bob Cratchit 9 Euan 10 Carol

QUIZ 300

• •

1 What is a Sopwith Camel?   Dromedary, Overcoat, Aeroplane

2 Which club did Alan Smith move to from Leeds United in May 2004? Liverpool, Manchester United, Newcastle United

3 Which film won Tom Hanks his first Oscar?   *Forrest Gump*, *Philadelphia*, *Sleepless In Seattle*

4 What is the alternative name for the buttonwood tree?   Larch, Sycamore, Poplar

5 What did Marilyn Monroe claim to wear in bed? A smile, Chanel No 5, Jewellery

6 Which city is home to the Petronas Towers? Sydney, Kuala Lumpur, Budapest

7 What was cappucino coffee named after?   Card game, Hotel, Order of Monks

8 According to the lyrics of the song what does Mack the Knife wear on his hands?   Fancy rings, Fancy gloves, Fancy mittens

9 What is the Muslim equivalent of the Red Cross? Red Crescent, Red Moon, Red Star

10 What did Paul McCartney wear on his feet on the album cover of Abbey Road?   Nothing, Mountain Boots, Slippers

ANSWERS

1. Aeroplane 2. Manchester United 3. *Philadelphia* 4. Sycamore 5. Chanel No 5 6. Kuala Lumpur 7. Order of Monks 8. Fancy gloves 9. Red Crescent 10 Nothing